WORLD PRAISE

MUSIC EDITION

Edited by

David Peacock and Geoff Weaver

Jubilate Hymns

Marshall Pickering
An Imprint of HarperCollins*Publishers*

Marshall Pickering is an imprint of
HarperCollins*Religious*
Part of HarperCollins*Publishers*
77–85 Fulham Palace Road,
Hammersmith, London W6 8JB

This edition first published in Great Britain in 1993 by Marshall Pickering

Reprinted: 96 95 94 93
Impression number: 10 9 8 7 6 5 4 3 2 1

The compilers assert the moral right to be identified as the compilers of this work

ISBN 0 551 04000 9

Words only (pack of 10) ISBN 0 551 04001 7

Music and text set by Barnes Music Engraving Ltd, East Sussex, England
Printed and bound in Great Britain by Scotprint Limited, Musselburgh, Edinburgh

A catalogue record for this book is available from the British Library

Other books edited by the Jubilate group:

Available from HarperCollins	Available from Hodder Headline
Carol Praise	Hymns for Today's Church
Play Carol Praise	Church Family Worship
Let's Praise!	Carols for Today
Come Rejoice!	Psalms for Today
The Wedding Book	Songs from the Psalms
Lollipops	
The Dramatised Bible	
Prayers for the People	

Foreword

by the Chairman of the
Baptist World Alliance Worship Commission

Wherever Baptists gather – there is music and singing!

We have come a long way from the seventeenth century, when some Baptists showed their opposition to congregational hymn singing by stating that to 'permit singing by art of pleasant tunes, and you will bring music and even instruments back again into public worship . . . and then farewell to all solemnity'.

The hymns at the first Baptist World Congress held in 1905 included *All people that on earth do dwell* (England 1561) and *Blest be the tie that binds* (England 1772). And in the years that followed, the hymns and music for Baptist World Congress gatherings were largely drawn from the European and North American Baptist traditions.

In preparation for the 1995 Baptist World Alliance Congress in Buenos Aires the Worship Commission of the Baptist World Alliance asked David Peacock to collect music material from around the world in order to gain a global perspective on the wealth of worship music being used. David enlisted the help of Geoff Weaver, of the Church Missionary Society, and these collections of world praise items will progress through the European Baptist Federation's Congress in Norway in 1994 to the World Baptist Congress in Argentina in 1995.

Congregations who use music drawn from their own culture have a vibrancy and relevance within their worship; the worship flows from the heart. Many of these songs have been born in suffering and pain, and Christians in the West are learning to be recipients rather than donors of a fresh and rich worship vocabulary. This book is offered to all Christians around the world as a major resource for praise and worship.

David Coffey
September 1993

Preface

World Praise is a unique collection of material drawn from worshipping communities around the world. Here you will find material from African, Asian, Caribbean, European and South American churches – music that crosses denominations and traditions. The items have been chosen because of their ability to travel beyond their place of origination. They range from lively expressions of praise to quiet songs of confession and poignant items yearning for justice.

This is the first of three volumes of world worship music. In this volume we have drawn primarily on material from outside North America and Western Europe. Texts for most items are in both the original language and in English. In the English translation we have attempted to convey the original meaning as far as possible while trying to fit the text into a regular metrical pattern. We would encourage congregations to sing in the original language wherever appropriate.

The music is arranged with straightforward accompaniments that attempt to capture the authentic nature of each song. Vocal parts, where appropriate, are arranged in four parts. Guitar chords are given for most songs. Each item has performance notes so that congregations are able to sing the different styles of music with integrity.

The stimulus for this book comes from the Baptist World Alliance's Worship Commission which is involved in researching different perspectives on worship around the world. A good number of the items have never been published before.

In recent years, Christians in the West have begun to see mission as more of a partnership – a giving and receiving between different parts of the Body of Christ. Those of us who have so many resources of our own have often found it difficult to imagine that we might need to receive from others – or indeed that there might be hidden riches for us to receive. **World Praise** is an opportunity to enrich our worship. In prayer, we can often react intellectually to news of suffering abroad. However, when we sing the songs of Christians in other parts of the world, we are able to enter more fully into their joys and pains. Then we truly understand what Paul means when he writes 'rejoice with those who rejoice and mourn with those who mourn' (*Romans 12:15*).

World Praise can easily be used as a supplement to a congregation's existing repertoire. The book is ideally suited to churches desiring a global perspective within their worship and a broad repertoire for their worship expression. Many items work well alongside hymns and worship-songs.

World Praise is also useful for missionary services, for international conferences and events, for cross-cultural events, and for congregations made up of a range of nationalities and cultures.

David Peacock and Geoff Weaver
Editors

Legal Information
and Acknowledgements

We are grateful to all those who have provided material for this volume. We thank especially those belonging to Baptist churches around the world and to mission partners of the Church Missionary Society, from whom many of the songs have been collected. We particularly owe our thanks to Michael Perry for his expertise in adapting the texts; to Joanna Bennett and Jane Peacock for preparing the material ready for publication. For the major task of copyright clearance we are deeply grateful to Stanley Grant.

Every effort has been made to trace copyright owners, and apologies are extended to anyone whose rights have inadvertently not been acknowledged. Any omissions or inaccuracies of copyright details will be corrected in future editions.

Reprinting
Those seeking to reprint material in this book should refer to the addresses given at the back.

David Peacock and Geoff Weaver
Editors

1 A BABY WAS BORN IN BETHLEHEM

CARIBBEAN

Words and music: Ivor Golby
arranged Noël Tredinnick

1 A baby was born in Bethlehem, a baby was born in Bethlehem, a baby was born in Bethlehem – it was Jesus Christ, our Lord.

2 They laid him in a manger, They laid him in a manger, They laid him in a manger – where the ox-en feed on hay.

3 Some shepherds heard the glad tidings, Some shepherds heard the glad tidings, Some shepherds heard the glad tidings – from an angel in the sky.

The calypso and the Caribbean are almost synonymous.
Feel the rhythm here rather than counting it mechanically.

4　They left their flocks a-sleeping . . .
　　and hurried to Bethlehem.
　　　Gloria, gloria . . .

5　Three wise men came from far lands . . .
　　they were guided by a star.
　　　Gloria, gloria . . .

6　They laid their gifts before him . . .
　　and worshipped on bended knee.
　　　Gloria, gloria . . .

7　Then everybody be happy . . .
　　on the birthday of our Lord!
　　　Gloria, gloria . . .

2 ALL WHO ARE THIRSTY

PHILIPPINES

Words: from Isaiah 55
Michael Perry
Music: Mutya Lopez Solis
arranged Geoff Weaver

Steadily ♩ = 92

1 All who are thirs - ty,_____ come to the Lord,
2 Why spend your mon - ey,_____ yet have no bread;
3 Call on God's mer - cy_____ while he is near,
4 Where once were bri - ers,_____ flo-wers will grow,

all who are hun - gry,_____ feed on his word;
why work for noth - ing?_____ Trust God in-stead!
turn from your e - vil,_____ come with-out fear;
where lives were bar - ren,_____ riv - ers will flow:

buy with-out pay - ing,_____ food with-out price,
He will pro-vide you_____ rich - est of food:
ask him for par - don =_____ grace will a-bound!
praise to our Sav - iour:_____ grace and re-nown –

> Typically Filipino in its blend of joy and melancholy, this song speaks of
> the hope that Filipino Christians, so often hit by suffering and oppression,
> have in Christ. A guitar accompaniment is very effective here.

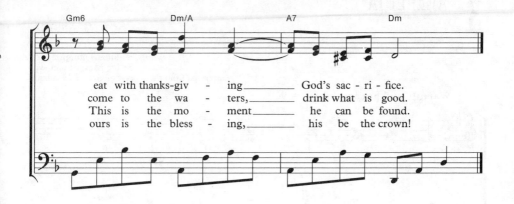

eat with thanks-giv - ing_____ God's sac - ri - fice.
come to the wa - ters,_____ drink what is good.
This is the mo - ment_____ he can be found.
ours is the bless - ing,_____ his be the crown!

1 All who are thirsty, come to the Lord,
    all who are hungry, feed on his word;
    buy without paying, food without price,
    eat with thanksgiving God's sacrifice.

2 Why spend your money, yet have no bread;
    why work for nothing? Trust God instead!
    He will provide you richest of food:
    come to the waters, drink what is good.

3 Call on God's mercy while he is near,
    turn from your evil, come without fear;
    ask him for pardon – grace will abound!
    This is the moment he can be found.

4 Where once were briers, flowers will grow,
    where lives were barren, rivers will flow:
    praise to our Saviour: grace and renown –
    ours is the blessing, his be the crown!

3 ALLELUIA

SOUTH AFRICA

Words: traditional liturgical text
Music: unknown
transcribed from the singing of George Mxadana

Warmly and purposefully ♩ = 96

Al – le – lu – ia,   al – le – lu – ia.

Al – le – lu – ia,   al – le – lu – ia.   Al –

– le – lu – ia,   al – le – lu – ia.   Al –

– le – lu – ia,   al – le – lu – ia.

> South Africans are renowned for the richness of their unaccompanied singing.
> This should be sung reflectively rather than boisterously, and should be unaccompanied.

4 AMAHORO BENEDATA

Peace be with you

RWANDA

Words: unknown
Music: unknown
arranged Geoff Weaver

Medium tempo ♩ = 104

A - ma - ho - ro be - ne - da - ta   a - ma - ho - ro.
Peace be with you, Christ-ian peo - ple, peace be with   you.

A - ma - ho - ro kwa Ye - su,   a - ma - ho - ro – hal - le - lu - jah!
Peace be with   you through Je - sus, peace be with you – hal - le - lu - jah!

1 LEADER ALL	*Amahoro benedata amahoro. Amahoro kwa Yesu, amahoro – hallelujah!*	1 LEADER ALL	Peace be with you, Christian people, peace be with you. Peace be with you through Jesus, peace be with you – hallelujah!
2 LEADER ALL	*Urekundo, benedata urekundo . . .*	2 LEADER ALL	Love be with you, Christian people, love be with you . . .
3 LEADER ALL	*Munezero, benedata munezero . . .*	3 LEADER ALL	Joy be with you, Christian people, joy be with you . . .

A song suitable for the exchanging of the peace. Like so many African songs, it is unaccompanied and has a leader-response format. The response could be harmonized simply.

5 AMEN, SIAKUDUMISA!

Amen, we praise your name, O God

SOUTH AFRICA

Words: unknown
Music: attributed to S. C. Molefe,
as taught by George Mxadana
arranged Dave Dargie

At a steady pace ♩ = 120

LEADER
Ma - si thi!
Sing prai - ses!

Ma - si thi!
Sing prai - ses!

S. A.
A-men, si - a - ku - du - mi - sa!
A-men, we praise your name, O God!

T. B.

DESCANT
A-men, si - a - ku - du - mi - sa!
A-men, we praise your name, O God!

ECHO
A-men, si - a - ku - du - mi - sa!
A-men, we praise your name, O God!

ECHO

This exuberant song of praise was written by S. C. Molefe at a workshop in South Africa. The harmonies are rich and the 'masithi' from the leader is an encouragement to the congregation. It is very effective in procession, either at the start or at the end of a service.

Music arrangement: © Dave Dargie, Melusinenstrasse 13,
8000 München 80, Germany

6 AMEN, ALLELUIA!

SOUTH AFRICA

Words: traditional
Music: traditional, transcribed from the singing
of George Mxadana and Monica Mothile

Originally a wedding song, this is a favourite 'going out' song in the worship of the Independent Churches of South Africa. It requires a strong rhythmic sense but should not be sung too quickly.

7 BANI NGYETI BA YAWE
Let us praise the Lord our God

CAMEROON

Words: unknown
Music: unknown
arranged Geoff Weaver

Bani ngyeti Ba Yawe / Let us praise the Lord our God,
ba-ni ngye-ti Ba Ya-we / let us praise the Lord our God,
ba-ni ngye-ti Ba Ya-we. A-men. / let us praise the Lord our God. A-men.
Hal-le-lu-yah, Hal-le-lu-jah,
hal-le-lu-yah, hal-le-lu-yah. A-men.
hal-le-lu-jah, hal-le-lu-jah. A-men.

Bani ngyeti Ba Yawe
bani ngyeti Ba Yawe
bani ngyeti Ba Yawe.
Amen.

Let us praise the Lord our God,
let us praise the Lord our God,
let us praise the Lord our God.
Amen.

Halleluyah, halleluyah,
halleluyah. Amen.

Hallelujah, hallelujah,
hallelujah. Amen.

A joyful West African song which lends itself well to added descants, rhythms and verses and indeed dance. Freedom and exuberance are the watch-words here.

8 BOLO JAY, MIKAR JAY

Sing my soul, sing to God

INDIA

Words: unknown
Music: unknown
arranged Geoff Weaver

This gentle and simple song of praise was sung to the arranger by an Indian pastor's wife. The verse could very effectively be sung as a solo, the chorus by all.

bha - r dey   a - pa - ni___ preeth.   Te - rey   pre - m ke   ga - ye___
with your love,   may I love you more.
free from guilt,   may I love you more.   Let me   dai - ly___   sing_ of your

geeth,   te - rey   pre - m ke   ga - ye___   geeth.
love,   let   me   dai - ly___   sing___   of your   love.

D.C.

Bolo jay, mikar jay,
bolo jay eshu ki jay;
Bolo jay, bolo jay,
bolo jay eshu ki jay;
bolo jay, jay, jay.

1 *Prem ki teri yehi reeth*
   mun may bhar dey apani preeth.
   Prem ki teri . . .
   Terey prem ke gaye geeth,
   terey prem ke gaye geeth.
      Bolo jay . . .

   Sing my soul, sing to God,
   sing to God, hallelujah!
   Sing my soul, sing to God,
   sing to God, hallelujah, hallelujah!

1 Your love is boundless, wide as the ocean,
   fill my heart with your love, may I love you more.
   Your love . . .
   Let me daily sing of your love,
   let me daily sing of your love.
      Sing my soul . . .

2 You shed your precious blood to give redemption,
   now that I am free from guilt, may I love you more.
   You shed . . .
   Let me daily sing of your love,
   let me daily sing of your love.
      Sing my soul . . .

9 BY THE BABYLONIAN RIVERS

LATVIA

Words: from Psalm 137
Ewald Bash
Music: Latvian melody
arranged Geoff Weaver

1 By the Babylonian rivers we sat down in grief and wept; hung our harps upon a willow, mourned for Zion while we slept.
2 There our captors, in derision, did require of us a song; so we sat with staring vision and the days were hard and long.
3 How shall we sing the Lord's song in a strange and bitter land; can our voices veil the sorrow? Lord God hear your lonely band.
4 Let your cross be benediction for all bound in tyranny; by the power of resurrection loose them from captivity.

This melancholy Latvian folk melody reflects beautifully the desolation of the exiles. This is very effective when sung unaccompanied or with simple guitar accompaniment.

ISRAEL

Words: from Psalm 137
Music: Israeli folk melody
arranged Geoff Weaver

The source of this very effective canon is uncertain. As with all canons, ensure that it is well known before dividing the congregation.

11 CANTAD AL SEÑOR

O sing to the Lord

Words: anonymous
translated Gerhard Cartford
Music: Brazilian folksong
arranged Christopher Norton

Brightly ♩. = 70

Lyrics beneath the music:

1 Can -
1 O

- tad al Señ - or un cán - ti - co nue - vo. Can-
(2) - que el Señ - or ha he - cho pro - di - gios. Por -
sing to the Lord, O sing God a new song; O
(2) God is the Lord and God has done won - ders, for

- tad al Señ - or un cán - ti - co nue - vo. Can - tad al Señ -
- que el Señ - or ha he - cho pro - di - gios. Por - que el Señ -
sing to the Lord, O sing God a new song; O sing to the
God is the Lord and God has done won - ders; for God is the

- or un cán - ti - co nue - vo. ¡Can - tad al Señ - or, can -
- or ha he - cho pro - di - gios. ¡Can - tad al Señ - or, can -
Lord, O sing God a new song – O sing to our God, O
Lord and God has done won - ders – O sing to our God, O

A lively Brazilian worship song that can be enhanced
by a range of percussive sounds and lively dancing.

-tad	al	Señ -	or!_____	2 Por- - or!_____
-tad	al	Señ -	or!_____	3 Can-
sing	to	our	God!_____	2 For God._____
sing	to	our	God!_____	3 So

1 *Cantad al Señor un cántico nuevo.*
   Cantad al Señor un cántico nuevo.
   Cantad al Señor un cántico nuevo.
   ¡Cantad al Señor, cantad al Señor!

2 *Porque el Señor ha hecho prodigios.*
   Porque el Señor ha hecho prodigios.
   Porque el Señor ha hecho prodigios.
   ¡Cantad al Señor, cantad al Señor!

3 *Cantad al Señor, alabadle con arpa.*
   Cantad al Señor, alabadle con arpa.
   Cantad al Señor, alabadle con arpa.
   ¡Cantad al Señor, cantad al Señor!

4 *Es el que nos da el Espiritu Santo.*
   Es el que nos da el Espiritu Santo.
   Es el que nos da el Espiritu Santo.
   ¡Cantad al Señor, cantad al Señor!

5 *¡Jesus es Señor! ¡Amen, aleluya!*
   ¡Jesus es Señor! ¡Amen, aleluya!
   ¡Jesus es Señor! ¡Amen, aleluya!
   ¡Cantad al Señor, cantad al Señor!

1 O sing to the Lord, O sing God a new song;
   O sing to the Lord, O sing God a new song;
   O sing to the Lord, O sing God a new song –
   O sing to our God, O sing to our God!

2 For God is the Lord and God has done wonders,
   for God is the Lord and God has done wonders;
   for God is the Lord and God has done wonders –
   O sing to our God, O sing to our God!

3 So dance for our God and blow all the trumpets,
   so dance for our God and blow all the trumpets;
   so dance for our God and blow all the trumpets –
   O sing to our God, O sing to our God!

4 O shout to our God, who gave us the Spirit,
   O shout to our God, who gave us the Spirit;
   O shout to our God, who gave us the Spirit –
   O sing to our God, O sing to our God!

5 For Jesus is Lord, Amen! Alleluia!
   For Jesus is Lord, Amen! Alleluia!
   For Jesus is Lord, Amen! Alleluia!
   O sing to our God, O sing to our God!

12 CHU YŎ SA SŬ MI SHI NAEN MUL
My soul longs for you

KOREA

Words: from Psalm 42
Music: Geonyong Lee

Expressively

PART 1

Chu yŏ_____ sa sŭ mi_____ shi naen mul_____
My soul_____ longs for you,_____ O my God,_____

PART 2

Chu yŏ_____ sa sŭ mi_____ shi naen mul_
My soul_____ longs for you,_____ O my God,

ch'at tŭt_____ nae nŏk si chu rŭl ch'at sŭm ni da._____
as a deer_____ longs for flow - ing streams, for flow-ing streams._____

_ ch'at tŭt_____ nae nŏk si chu rŭl ch'at sŭm ni
_ my God,_____ longs for flow - ing streams, thirsts for my

_ Kal kŭ p'an nae yŏng hon i sa ra ge shin
_ My soul thirsts for God, for God, the liv - ing God:

da. Kal kŭ p'an nae yŏng hon i sa ra ge
God, for my God, the liv - ing God: when shall I

chu_____ ni mŭl ŏn che na poe o ri kka._____
when shall I come to be - hold_ the face of my God?_____

shin chu ni mŭl ŏn che na poe o ri kka.
come, shall I come, to be - hold_ the face of my God?

> This haunting two-part setting of words from Psalm 42 is best sung unac-
> companied, following the natural accents of the text. Geonyong Lee has waited and
> yearned for justice and re-unification in his country of Korea, and this song
> powerfully reflects that longing.

13 COME NOW, O PRINCE OF PEACE

KOREA

Words: Geonyong Lee;
paraphrased by Marion Pope; altered
Music: 1991 Geonyong Lee

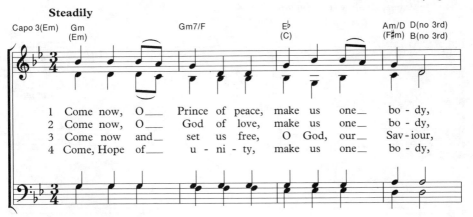

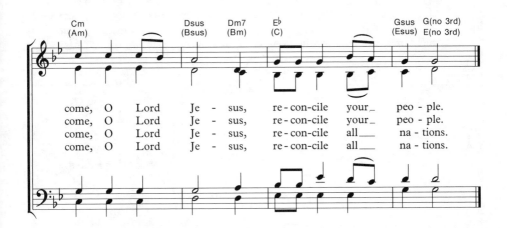

1 Come now, O Prince of peace,
make us one body,
come, O Lord Jesus,
reconcile your people.

2 Come now, O God of love,
make us one body,
come, O Lord Jesus,
reconcile your people.

3 Come now and set us free,
O God, our Saviour,
come, O Lord Jesus,
reconcile all nations.

4 Come, Hope of unity,
make us one body,
come, O Lord Jesus,
reconcile all nations.

> For most Korean Christians re-unification of North and South Korea is their priority, and their urgent prayer. Geonyong Lee, one of the leading contemporary composers in Korea, has long identified himself with this struggle. Note how the dissonant harmonies paint the discord within the nation. This is very effective when sung unaccompanied.

14 CORDERO NG DIYOS
O Lamb of God

PHILIPPINES

AGNES DEI

Words: traditional
Music: unknown
arranged David Peacock

Expressively with rhythm ♩ = 100

Cor - de - ro ng Diyos na na - ga - a - lis, ng mg-
O Lamb of God you take a - way the

-a ka - sa - la - nan ng san - li - bu - tan. Ma -
sins of the world, have mer - cy on us. Have

-a - wa ka, ma - a - wa ka, sa a -
mer - cy, have mer - cy, have mer -

- cy, min. Cor - de - ro ng
- cy, Lord. O Lamb of

A beautiful song from the Philippines, where the long history of suffering makes this prayer for mercy so poignant.

Diyos na na-ga - a - lis, ng mg-a ka-sa - la-nan ng
God you_ take a - way the_ sins of the world, have

san-li - bu - tan. I - pag - ka - loob_____ mo ang
mer-cy on us. Have mer - cy,_ have mer -

i - yong ka - pa - ya - pa - an._____
- cy, and_ grant, O grant us peace._____

Cordero ng Diyos na nagaalis,
ng mga kasalanan ng sanlibutan.
Maawa ka, maawa ka, sa amin.

O Lamb of God you take away
the sins of the world, have mercy on us.
Have mercy, have mercy,
have mercy, Lord.

Cordero ng Diyos na nagaalis,
ng mga kasalanan ng sanlibutan.
Ipagkaloob mo ang iyong kapayapaan.

O Lamb of God you take away
the sins of the world, have mercy on us.
Have mercy, have mercy,
and grant, O grant us peace.

15 CRISTO VIVE
Christ is risen

ARGENTINA

Words: after Nicolas Martinez
Fred Kaan
Music: Pablo D. Sosa

Confidently

1 ¡Cris-to vi - ve, fue-ra el llan - to, los la - men - tos y el pe -
2 Que si Cris - to no vi - vie - ra va-na fue - ra nues-tra -
1 Christ is ris - en, Christ is liv - ing, dry your tears, be un - a -
2 If the Lord had ne - ver ris - en, we'd have noth - ing to be -

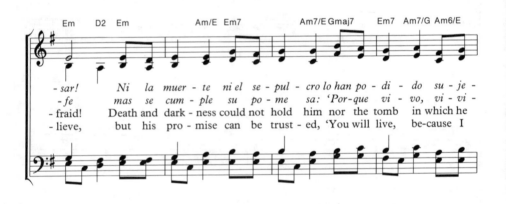

- sar! Ni la muer - te ni el se - pul - cro lo han po - di - do su - je -
- fe mas se cum - ple su po - me sa: 'Por-que vi - vo, vi - vi -
- fraid! Death and dark - ness could not hold him nor the tomb in which he
- lieve, but his pro - mise can be trust - ed, 'You will live, be-cause I

- tar. No bus - quéls en - tre los muer-tos al que siem-pre ha de vi -
- réis.' Si en A - dán en - tró la muer-te, por Jé - sus la vi-da en -
lay. Do not look a-mong the dead for one who lives for ev - er -
live.' As we share the death of Ad-am, so in Christ we live a -

> Coming out of a situation of oppression and anguish, reflected in the minor key, this Easter song brings hope; the spirit of the dance is never far away.

Music: © 1962 Asociacion Ediciones La Aurora,
BeanSunes 1823, 1244 Buenos Aires, Argentina

Words: © 1974 Stainer and Bell Ltd.
USA and Canada Hope Publishing Co., Carol Stream, Il 60188

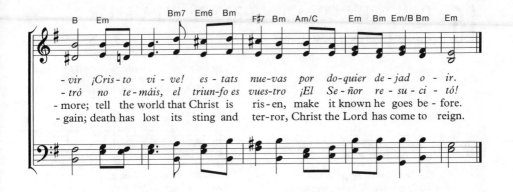

1 ¡Cristo vive, fuera el llanto, los lamentos y el pesar!
Ni la muerte ni el sepulcro lo han podido sujetar.
No busquéls en tre los muertos al que siempre ha de vivir
¡Cristo vive! estats nuevas por doquier dejad oir.

2 Que si Cristo no viviera vana fuera nuestrafe
mas se cumple su pome sa: 'Porque vivo, viviréis.'
Si en Adán entró la muerte, por Jésus la vida entró
no temáis, el triunfo es vuestro ¡El Señor resucitó!

3 Si es verdad que de la muerte el pecado es aguijón
no temáis pues Jesucristo nos da vida y salvacion.
Gracias demos al Dios Padre que nos da seguridad
que quien cree en Jesucristo vive por la eternidad.

1 Christ is risen, Christ is living,
dry your tears, be unafraid!
Death and darkness could not hold him
nor the tomb in which he lay.
Do not look among the dead
for one who lives for evermore;
tell the world that Christ is risen,
make it known he goes before.

2 If the Lord had never risen,
we'd have nothing to believe,
but his promise can be trusted,
'You will live, because I live.'
As we share the death of Adam,
so in Christ we live again;
death has lost its sting and terror,
Christ the Lord has come to reign.

3 Death has lost its old dominion:
let the world rejoice and shout!
Christ the firstborn of the living,
gives us life and leads us out.
Let us thank our God who causes
hope to spring up from the ground.
Christ is risen! Christ is giving
life eternal, life profound.

16 DANOS UN CORAZÓN GRANDE PARA AMAR
God, give us a new heart

EL SALVADOR

Words: from the Salvadorian
in this version Word & Music
Music arranged Christopher Norton

Chorus

Da - nos un co-ra - zón / gran-de pa-ra a - mar.
God, give us a new heart, / big e-nough to love;

Da - nos un co-ra - zón / fuer - te pa-ra lu - char.
God, give us a new heart, / strong e - nough to fight.

Fine

Verse

1 Gen - tes nue-vos, crea-do - res de la his - to-ria con - struc-
1 Re - newed peo-ple, cre-a - tors of his-tory— build - ers
2 Re - newed peo - ple,— strugg - ling in hope— thir - sty
3 Re - newed peo - ple,— lov - ing with-out li - mit— with-out re-

- to-res de nue-va hu-ma - ni - dad. Gen-tes neu-vos que vi - ven la e - xis-
of— a new hu-man-it - y; re-newed peo-ple who live— with ad-
pil - grims, seek-ing truth and light; re-newed peo-ple, now free from all their
- gard to race or price of place; re-newed peo - ple,— stand-ing by the

So great has been the suffering of the people of El Salvador that the prayer for a new heart, a heart which can love rather than hate, must be a very powerful one. There is strength and determination about this song, and the rhythms of the dance are never far below the surface.

El Salvadorian words: Copyright control
Music: Used by permission of Baptist Association of El Salvador   English words: © 1993 Word & Music / Jubilee Hymns

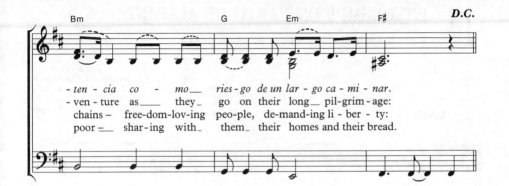

- ten - cia   co - mo__   ries - go de un lar - go ca - mi - nar.
- ven - ture as__   they_   go on their long__ pil - grim - age:
chains –   free - dom - lov - ing peo - ple, de - mand - ing li - ber - ty:
poor =__   shar - ing with_   them_   their homes and their bread.

Danos un corazón grande para amar.
Danos un corazón fuerte para luchar.

1 *Gentes nuevos, creadores de la historia*
   constructores de nueva humanidad.
   Gentes neuvos que viven la existencia
   como riesgo de un largo caminar.
      Danos . . .

2 *Gentes nuevos luhando en esperanza*
   caminantessedientes de verdad
   gentes nuevos sin frenos ni cadenas
   gentes libres que exigen libertad.
      Danos . . .

3 *Gentes nuevos amando sin fronteras*
   por encima de razas y lugar
   gentes nuevos al lado de los pobres
   compartiendo con ellos techo y pan.
      Danos . . .

      God, give us a new heart,
      big enough to love;
      God, give us a new heart,
      strong enough to fight.

1 Renewed people, creators of history –
   builders of a new humanity;
   renewed people who live with adventure
   as they go on their long pilgrimage:
      God, give us . . .

2 Renewed people, struggling in hope –
   thirsty pilgrims, seeking truth and light;
   renewed people, now free from all their chains –
   freedom-loving people, demanding liberty:
      God, give us . . .

3 Renewed people, loving without limit –
   without regard to race or price of place;
   renewed people, standing by the poor –
   sharing with them their homes and their bread.
      God, give us . . .

17 ENTONEMOS UN CANTO DE ALABANZA

Let us sing to the Lord a song of praise

GUATEMALA

Words: unknown
translated G. Lockwood
in this version Word & Music / Jubilate Hymns
Music: Alfredo Colom
arranged Christopher Norton

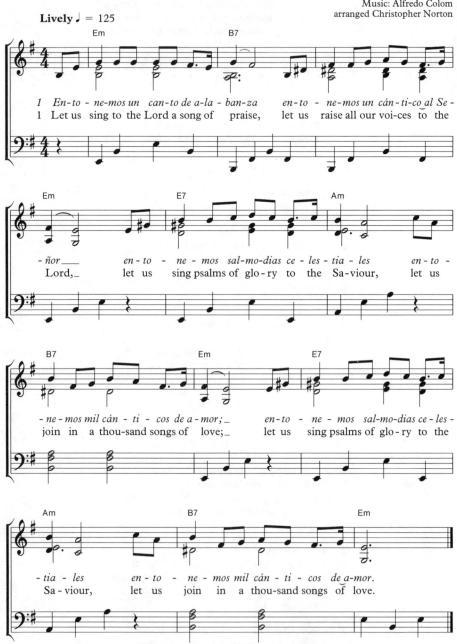

1 En-to - ne-mos un can-to de a-la - ban-za en-to - ne-mos un cán-ti-co al Se-
1 Let us sing to the Lord a song of praise, let us raise all our voi-ces to the

-ñor ___ en-to - ne - mos sal-mo-dias ce - les-tia - les en-to-
Lord, _ let us sing psalms of glo-ry to the Sa-viour, let us

- ne-mos mil cán - ti - cos de a-mor; _ en-to - ne - mos sal-mo-dias ce-les-
join in a thou-sand songs of love; _ let us sing psalms of glo-ry to the

- tia - les en-to - ne - mos mil cán - ti - cos de a-mor.
Sa - viour, let us join in a thou-sand songs of love.

A lively dance song which seems to cry out for guitars and light percussion accompaniment.
Don't be afraid to experiment with descants and harmonies.

1　*Entonemos un canto de alabanza*
　entonemos un cántico al Señor
　entonemos salmodias celestiales
　entonemos mil cánticos de amor;
　entonemos salmodias . . .

2　*Demos gracias al Padre por la vida,*
　demos gracias al Padre por Jesús.
　Y sigamos la senda de la gloria
　con la carga divina de la cruz;
　Y sigamos la senda . . .

3　*Demos gloria al Señor por este dia*
　por sus muchos cuidados, por su amor
　porque Dios en su gran misericordia
　nos dio vida en Jesús nuestro Señor;
　porque Dios . . .

1　Let us sing to the Lord a song of praise,
　let us raise all our voices to the Lord,
　let us sing psalms of glory to the Saviour,
　let us join in a thousand songs of love;
　　let us sing psalms of glory . . .

2　Thanks we give for the gift of life you grant us,
　thanks we give to our God for Jesus Christ –
　so let's follow the path that leads to glory,
　with the glorious burden of the cross;
　　so let's follow . . .

3　Let us take to ourselves the heavenly armour,
　let us use all love's weapons in our cause;
　we will fight for the right, till in the future
　we can say, 'We are more than conquerors!'
　　we will fight . . .

4　Glory give to our God for each new morning,
　for his wonderful blessings and his love:
　for our God in the goodness of his mercy
　gave us life, life in Jesus Christ our Lord;
　　for our God . . .

18 EWURADZE
Have mercy, Lord

GHANA

KYRIE

Music: unknown
arranged Geoff Weaver

Prayerfully ♩ = 100

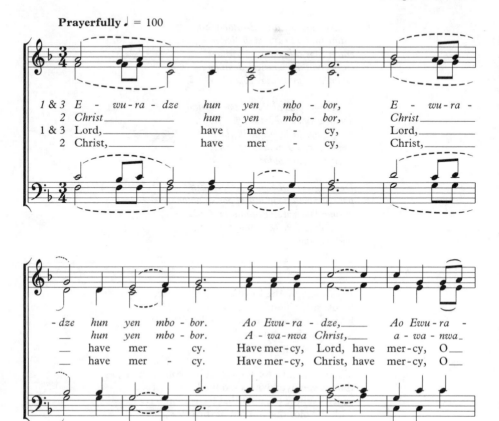

1 & 3 E - wu - ra - dze hun yen mbo - bor, E - wu - ra -
2 Christ_____ hun yen mbo - bor, Christ_____
1 & 3 Lord,_____ have mer - cy, Lord,_____
2 Christ,_____ have mer - cy, Christ,_____

- dze hun yen mbo - bor. Ao Ewu - ra - dze,_____ Ao Ewu - ra -
 ___ hun yen mbo - bor. A - wa - nwa Christ,_____ a - wa - nwa_
 ___ have mer - cy. Have mer - cy, Lord, have mer - cy, O__
 ___ have mer - cy. Have mer - cy, Christ, have mer - cy, O__

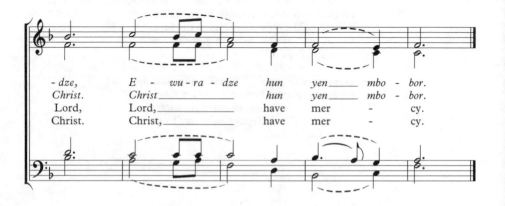

- dze, E - wu - ra - dze hun yen_____ mbo - bor.
Christ. Christ_____ hun yen_____ mbo - bor.
Lord, Lord,_____ have mer - cy.
Christ. Christ,_____ have mer - cy.

A beautiful song from Ghana, originally in the
Fante language. It should be sung a cappella

19 FATHER IN HEAVEN

PHILIPPINES

Words: D. T. Niles
Music: Elena G. Maquiso
arranged Geoff Weaver

HALAD

Unhurried ♩ = 88

1 Fa-ther in hea - ven,___ grant to your child - ren___ mer - cy and
(2) -deem - er,___ may we re - mem - ber___ your gra-cious
(3) -cend - ing, whose is the bless - ing, strength for the

bless - ing,___ songs ne - ver ceas - ing;___ love to u -
pas - sion,___ your re - sur - rec - tion:___ wor - ship we
wea - ry,___ help for the nee - dy:___ seal - ing Christ's

- nite us,___ grace to re - deem us,___ Fa - ther in
bring you,___ praise we shall sing you,___ Je - sus re -
Lord - ship, bless - ing our wor - ship, Spi - rit des -

1.2.
hea - ven,___ Fa - ther, our God. 2 Je - sus re -
- deem - er,___ Je - sus, our Lord. 3 Spi - rit des -
- cend - ing, Spi - rit a -

3.
- dored.

A beautiful hymn to the Trinity based on a Filipino folk song.
The words are by D. T. Niles, the great Sri Lankan Christian leader.

20 FOR THE BEAUTY OF THE EARTH

CHINA

Mo-Li-Hua

Words: F. Sandford Pierpoint
Music: Chinese folk song
adapted I-to-Loh

Worshipfully ♩ = 80

1 For the beau-ty_ of the earth, for the beau-ty_ of the skies,
2 For the beau-ty_ of each hour of the day and of the night,
3 For the joy of_ ear and eye, for the heart and mind's de-light,

for the love which from our birth o - ver_ and a -
hill and vale, and_ tree and flower, sun and moon and_
for the my - stic_ har - mo - ny link - ing_ sense to_

-round us_ lies,
stars of_ light, Christ our God, to you we_ raise
sound and sight,

This lovely Chinese folk song, used by Puccini in his opera 'Turandot', is a song about flowers. It is appropriate therefore that it should be sung as a hymn of thanksgiving for God's creation. Be particularly sensitive to the ebb and flow of the phrases.

this our sac-ri-fice of praise, this our sac - ri - fice_ of praise.

1 For the beauty of the earth,
  for the beauty of the skies,
  for the love which from our birth
  over and around us lies,
    Christ our God, to you we raise
    this our sacrifice of praise,
    this our sacrifice of praise.

2 For the beauty of each hour
  of the day and of the night,
  hill and vale, and tree and flower,
  sun and moon and stars of light,
    Christ our God . . .

3 For the joy of ear and eye,
  for the heart and mind's delight,
  for the mystic harmony
  linking sense to sound and sight,
    Christ our God . . .

4 For the joy of human love,
  brother, sister, parent, child,
  friends on earth and friends above,
  pleasures pure and undefiled,
    Christ our God . . .

5 For each perfect gift divine
  to our race so freely given,
  joys bestowed by love's design,
  flowers of earth and fruits of heaven,
    Christ our God . . .

21 FREE TO SERVE

Words and music: Tom Colvin
arranged David Peacock

Confidently, but not too fast ♩ = 100

Chorus

Free to serve, yes, free to serve, Christ has set us___ free___ to serve; free to serve, yes, free to serve, all in Christ are___ free to serve.

Fine Verse

1 When we walk a-lone and we work for self, when we make our plans just to in-crease our wealth; need-y neigh-bours there by the

2 But that lone-ly road leads to sla-ve-ry, life is full of fear, the end we can-not see; Christ has set us free, he has

3 Ev-ery pass-er-by is a friend to love, ev-ery one in need some-one in Christ to serve; fair so-ci-e-ty, hu-man

Singers may follow the three-part harmony as scored.

> A Ghanaian melody which in its directness and its syncopated rhythms captures the joy of freedom.
> A drum accompaniment will help to give the music an authentically Ghanaian flavour.

road-side cry, but we pass them by and take the o-ther side.____
shown the way – lov-ing, serv-ing o-thers brings us li-ber-ty.____
u – ni-ty – love is means and end, and lov-ing sets us free!____

Free to serve, yes, free to serve,
Christ has set us free to serve;
free to serve, yes, free to serve,
all in Christ are free to serve.

1   When we walk alone and we work for self,
when we make our plans just to increase our wealth;
needy neighbours there by the roadside cry,
but we pass them by and take the other side.
    Free to serve . . .

2   But that lonely road leads to slavery,
life is full of fear, the end we cannot see;
Christ has set us free, he has shown the way –
loving, serving others brings us liberty.
    Free to serve . . .

3   Every passer-by is a friend to love,
every one in need someone in Christ to serve;
fair society, human unity –
love is means and end, and loving sets us free!
    Free to serve . . .

22 GLORIA

PERU

Words and music: unknown

Lively but not too quickly

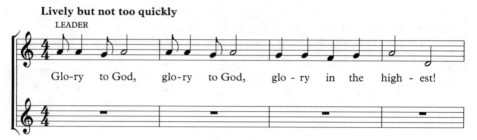

LEADER

Glo-ry to God, glo-ry to God, glo-ry in the high - est!

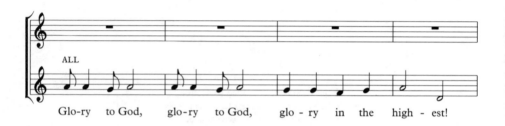

ALL

Glo-ry to God, glo-ry to God, glo - ry in the high - est!

To God be glo-ry for-ev - er!

To God be glo-ry for-ev - er!

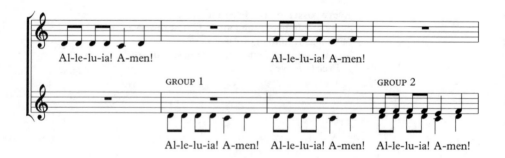

Al-le-lu-ia! A-men!   Al-le-lu-ia! A-men!

GROUP 1   GROUP 2

Al-le-lu-ia! A-men! Al-le-lu-ia! A-men! Al-le-lu-ia! A-men!

> This is ideal for celebrations and for any festive occasion. There are
> many ways of performing the Alleluias – feel free to experiment and to
> extend them. The song should be rhythmic but not too quick.

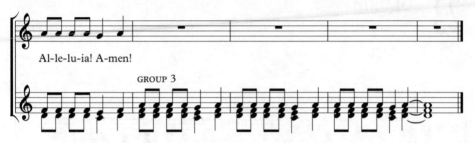

Al-le-lu-ia! A-men!

GROUP 3

Al-le-lu-ia! A-men! Al-le-lu-ia! A-men! Al-le-lu-ia! A-men! Al-le-lu-ia! A-men!_

LEADER	Glory to God, glory to God, glory in the highest!
ALL	Glory to God, glory to God, glory in the highest!
LEADER	To God be glory forever!
ALL	To God be glory forever!
LEADER	Alleluia! Amen!
GROUP 1	Alleluia! Amen!
LEADER	Alleluia! Amen!
GROUPS 1, 2	Alleluia! Amen!
LEADER	Alleluia! Amen!
GROUPS 1, 2, 3	Alleluia! Amen!
ALL	Alleluia! Amen! Alleluia! Amen!

23 GLORIA

ARGENTINA

Music: Pablo Sosa

Glo - ria, glo - ria, glo - ria en las al - tur - as a Dios!
Glo - ry, glo - ry, glo - ry, glo - ry be to God on high!

Y en la tie - rra paz pa - ra aque - llos que a - ma el Se - ñor.____
And on earth__ peace to the peo - ple in whom God is well pleased.

Gloria, gloria, gloria
en las alturas a Dios!
Gloria . . .
Y en la tierra paz para aquellos
que ama el Señor.
Y en la tierra . . .

Glory, glory, glory,
glory be to God on high!
Glory . . .
And on earth peace to the people
in whom God is well pleased.
And on earth . . .

Pablo Sosa is an Argentinian pastor and a prolific composer of new worship songs, often making use of folk dance rhythms and idioms. This Gloria uses the alternating § ¾ of the cueca, one of the national dances of Argentina, in recent times danced by women whose husbands have 'disappeared'. It should be sung lightly, rhythmically and unaccompanied, with a light percussion accompaniment.

24 HALLE, HALLELUJAH

CARIBBEAN

Words: traditional
Music: unknown
arranged Geoff Weaver

Lively ♩ = 112

Hal - le, hal - le, hal - le - lu - jah!

Hal - le, hal - le, hal - le - lu - jah!
hal - le - lu - jah

Hal - le, hal - le, hal - le - lu - jah! Hal - le -

to repeat / last time

- lu - jah, hal - le - lu - jah! ___ - jah! ___
hal - le - lu - jah

A song from the Caribbean, where many people are uninhibited in expressing their worship.

25 HALELUYA! PELO TSA RONA

Alleluia! we sing your praises

SOUTH AFRICA

Words: African origin
collected and edited by Anders Nyberg
Music: African melody
scored by Notman KB, Ljungsbro
and Lars Parkman

Confidently

Chorus

Ha - le - lu-ya! Pe - lo tsa ro-na, di tha - bi - le ka - o - fe -
Al - le - lu - ia! We sing your prais-es, all our hearts are filled with glad -

Fine

- la. Ha-le - lu-ya! Pe - lo tsa ro-na, di tha - bi - le ka - o - fe - la.
- ness. Al-le - lu - ia! We sing your prais-es, all our hearts are filled with glad-ness.

Verse

1 Ke Mo - re - na Je - so, ya re du - me - let -
2 O na na le bo mang? Le ba - ru - tu - wa
1 Christ the Lord to us said, 'I am wine, I am
2 Now he sends us all out, strong in faith, free of

An astonishing wealth of song has come out of South
Africa in recent years. Songs of pain and protest, but
also songs of faith and hope such as this one. The
syncopated rhythms should be strongly marked.

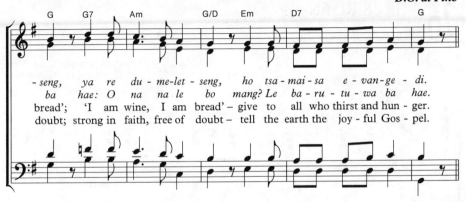

- seng, ya re du - me-let - seng, ho tsa - mai - sa e - van - ge - di.
ba hae: O na na le bo mang? Le ba - ru - tu - wa ba hae.
bread'; 'I am wine, I am bread' – give to all who thirst and hun - ger.
doubt; strong in faith, free of doubt – tell the earth the joy - ful Gos - pel.

Haleluya! Pelo tsa rona,
di thabile kaofela.
Haleluya . . .

1 *Ke Morena Jeso,*
ya re dumeletseng,
ya re dumeletseng,
ho tsamaisa evangedi.
Haleluya . . .

2 *O na na le bo mang?*
Le barutuwa ba hae:
O na na le bo mang?
Le barutuwa ba hae.
Haleluya . . .

Alleluia!
We sing your praises,
all our hearts
are filled with gladness.
Alleluia . . .

1 Christ the Lord to us said,
'I am wine, I am bread';
'I am wine, I am bread' –
give to all who thirst and hunger.
Alleluia . . .

2 Now he sends us all out,
strong in faith, free of doubt;
strong in faith, free of doubt –
tell the earth the joyful Gospel.
Alleluia . . .

26 HE IS RISEN

EAST AFRICA

Words and music: unknown
Music arranged David Peacock

Of uncertain origin, this song has many of the hallmarks of Africa – a leader calling for a response and lively rhythms to celebrate Christ's resurrection.

al - le - lu - ia! He is
al - le - lu - ia! He is
al - le - lu - ia! Al - le -

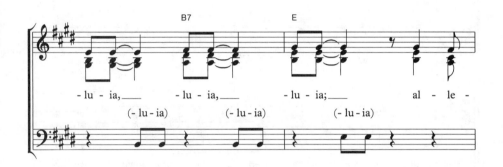

- lu - ia, ___ - lu - ia, ___ - lu - ia; ___ al - le -
(- lu - ia) (- lu - ia) (- lu - ia)

- lu - ia ___ life is come: he is ris - en, ___ ris - en, ___
(- lu-ia life is come:) (ris-en) (ris-en)

ris - en; ___ he is ris - en, ___ ris - en ─ the Lord!
(ris-en) (ris-en: ris-en ─ the Lord!)

27 HE CAME DOWN

CAMEROON

Words and music: unknown
arranged Geoff Weaver

Brightly ♩ = 60

1 He came down that we may have love; he
2 He came down that we may have peace; he
3 He came down that we may have joy: he

came down that we may have love; he came down that we may
came down that we may have peace; he came down that we may
came down that we may have joy: he came down that we may

have love;
have peace; hal - le - lu - jah for ev - er - more.
have joy:

(LEADER Why did he come?)

4 He came down that we may have power . . .

5 He came down that we may have hope . . .

A traditional Cameroonian song, which is often performed as a circle
dance with sweeping movements to suggest Christ's coming down.
The leader calls and encourages the congregation to respond.

28 HE WAS BORN A LITTLE CHILD

MALAWI

Words: from the Malawi
Helen Taylor
Music: unknown
arranged Geoff Weaver

Gently ♩ = 92

1 He was born a lit-tle child when he came to earth;
2 Shep-herds and their qui-et sheep saw the an-gel bright;
3 In the hills they left the lambs and the sleep-ing sheep;
4 'Shep-herds, you have run from a-far, breath-less, breath-less still:
5 'Shall we not a-dore him, ly-ing in the hay?

an-gels in the heavens a-bove told us of his birth.
shep-herds heard the an-gels sing-ing in the night.
down to Beth-le-hem they came, Je-sus Christ to seek.
who is car-ing for your sheep on the star-lit hill?'
Look, our sav-iour Je-sus, born for us to-day!'

Chorus

Mo-ther Ma-ry laid him in a cat-tle stall

lit-tle ba-by Je-sus who was Lord of all.

A gentle carol from Malawi, ideally sung unaccompanied.
Note the pentatonic (5 note scale) structure of the melody.

29 HOSANNA, HOSANNA

ZIMBABWE

Words: after Abraham Maraire
Word & Music
Music: Abraham Maraire

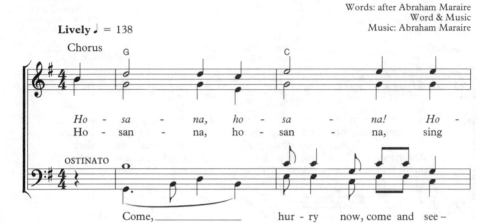

Lively ♩ = 138

Chorus

Ho - sa - na, ho - sa - na! Ho -
Ho - san - na, ho - san - na, sing

OSTINATO

Come,_____ hur - ry now, come and see –

- sa - na Mwa - na wa - Mwa - ri!
praise to the Son___ of God!

Fine

yes,_____ Je - sus comes on the road

Verse **D.C.**

1 Wo - pi - nda mu - Je - ru - sa - re - ma mu - sha wa - mwa - ri.
1 Je - ru - sa - lem, Je - ru - sa - lem, a - rise to greet your king:
2 Make clear the way, the sav - iour comes, your palms and prais - es bring:
3 With bless - ings come and hail the Lord, come shout for joy and sing:

An exuberant African welcome to Christ, ideal for a Palm Sunday procession.
The rhythmic tenor and bass ostinato can be enhanced by other rhythmic patterns,
e.g.

During the verses, the men continue to sing the ostinato. However, it is suggested
they are tacet for verse 2. Normally sung unaccompanied.

30 HUMBLY IN YOUR SIGHT

MALAWI

Words and music: Tom Colvin
arranged Geoff Weaver

Easy movement ♩ = 96

Capo 3(D)

1 Hum-bly in your sight we come to - ge-ther, Lord: grant us now the
2 These our hearts are yours— we give them to you, Lord: pu - ri - fy our
3 These our ears are yours, we give them to you, Lord: o - pen them to
4 These our eyes are yours, we give them to you, Lord: may we al - ways

Alternative setting for verses 3 and 7.
Sopranos sing the words, lower voices hum

bless-ing of your pre - sence here.   3 These our ears are yours, we give them
love to make it like your own.   7 These our feet are yours, we give them
hear the gos-pel straight from you.
see this world as with your sight.

to you, Lord: o - pen them to hear the gos-pel straight from you.
to you, Lord: may we al-ways walk the path of light with you.

5   These our hands are yours, we give them to you, Lord:
    give them strength and skill to work and build for you.

6   These our tongues are yours, we give them to you, Lord:
    may we speak your healing words of light and truth.

7   These our feet are yours, we give them to you, Lord:
    may we always walk the path of light with you.

8   Our whole selves are yours, we give them to you, Lord:
    take us now and keep us safe for evermore.

A simple Malawian folk song with simple harmonies,
effective when sung as people gather for worship

31 HWAYAN YA-MWARI
O Lamb of God

ZIMBABWE

AGNUS DEI

Words: traditional
Music: Emmanuel Ribeiro

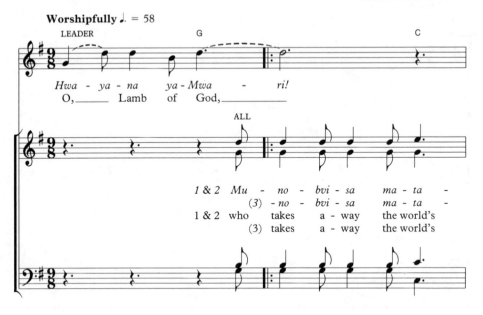

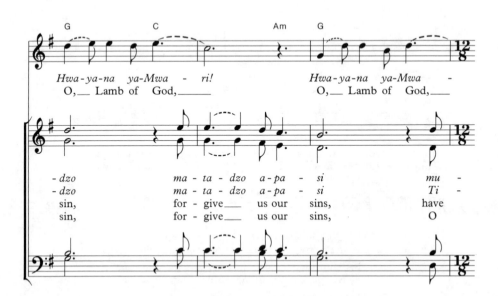

> The traditional African leader-response pattern
> is used effectively in this beautiful song.

1 LEADER *Hwayana ya-Mwari!*
  ALL   *Munobvisa matadzo*
  LEADER *Hwayana ya-Mwari!*
  ALL   *matadzo apasi*
  LEADER *Hwayana ya-Mwari!*
  ALL   *mutinzwi reiwo tsitsi!*

2 LEADER *Hwayana ya-Mwari!*
  ALL   *Munobvisa matadzo*
  LEADER *Hwayana ya-Mwari!*
  ALL   *matadzo apasi*
  LEADER *Hwayana ya-Mwari!*
  ALL   *mutinzwi reiwo tsitsi!*

3 LEADER *Hwayana ya-Mwari!*
  ALL   *Munobvisa matadzo*
  LEADER *Hwayana ya-Mwari!*
  ALL   *matadzo apasi*
  LEADER *Hwayana ya-Mwari!*
  ALL   *Tipeiwo rugare!*

1 LEADER O, Lamb of God,
  ALL   who takes away the world's sin,
  LEADER O, Lamb of God,
  ALL   forgive us our sins,
  LEADER O, Lamb of God,
  ALL   have mercy upon us,
          Lamb of God.

2 LEADER O, Lamb of God,
  ALL   who takes away the world's sin,
  LEADER O, Lamb of God,
  ALL   forgive us our sins,
  LEADER O, Lamb of God,
  ALL   have mercy upon us,
          Lamb of God.

3 LEADER O, Lamb of God,
  ALL   who takes away the world's sin,
  LEADER O, Lamb of God,
  ALL   forgive us our sins,
  LEADER O, Lamb of God,
  ALL   O Jesus, grant us your peace.

32 I WILL SING UNTO THE LORD

NIGERIA

Words and music: unknown
arranged Geoff Weaver

With joy and rhythmic freedom ♩ = 112

I will sing un-to the Lord a joy-ful song, and
bless his name for the Lord is good;
I will sing un-to the Lord, I will sing un-to the Lord, I will

We heard this joyful song, rather reminiscent of Psalm 105 in its sentiments, sung with great verve and vitality by the Yorubas of Nigeria. Feel the rhythm rather than counting it, and don't be afraid to exercise freedom and creativity.

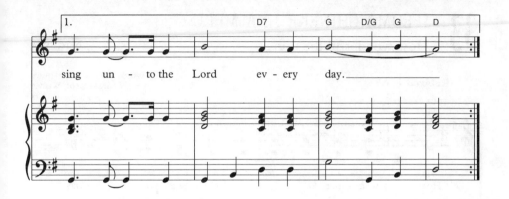

sing un - to the Lord ev – ery day._____

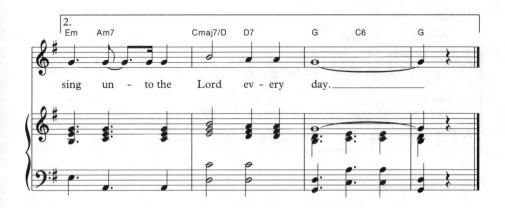

sing un - to the Lord ev – ery day._____

I will sing unto the Lord a joyful song,
and bless his name for the Lord is good;
I will sing unto the Lord a joyful song,
and bless his name for the Lord is good.
   I will sing unto the Lord,
   I will sing unto the Lord,
   I will sing unto the Lord every day.
   I will sing unto the Lord,
   I will sing unto the Lord,
   I will sing unto the Lord every day.

33 IFEOMA CHINEKE NNA MELU
How wonderful the things

NIGERIA

Words and music: unknown
arranged Geoff Weaver

This touching song of thanksgiving was sung to the arranger by a Nigerian pastor and his wife, who wanted to give thanks to God in all circumstances. Don't be too worried about meticulous observance of the rhythms.

Words: Nigerian Copyright control
Music arrangement: © 1993 Geoff Weaver / Jubilee Hymns   English © 1993 collected Geoff Weaver / Jubilee Hymns

34 IMELA
We thank you

Words and music:
Christ Church Gospel Band, Umani-Enugu
arranged Iona Community

Brightly

I - me - la,   i - me - la,   i - me - la,   O - ka - ka.
We thank you,   thank you Lord,   we thank you,   our great God.

I - me - la,   Chi - ne - ke.   I - me - le   On - y'o - ma.
We thank you,   gra-cious Lord,   we thank you,   our great God.

Imela, imela, imela, Okaka.
Imela, Chineke. Imele Ony'oma.

We thank you, thank you Lord,
we thank you, our great God.
We thank you, gracious Lord,
we thank you, our great God.

An Igbo song of thanksgiving, popular all over Nigeria. It requires freedom of expression, movement, handclaps, drumbeats and many repetitions to capture the authentic Nigerian flavour.

Words and music: © 1990 Christ Church Gospel Band, Box 4234
Umani-Enugu, Anambra State, Nigeria,
as taught by Mrs Unoaku Ekwegbalu

35 IN A STABLE

SPAIN

ESTA NOCHE

Words: Michael Perry
Music: Spanish carol melody
arranged Tom Cunningham

1 In a sta-ble,___ in a man-ger, lies a ba-by =___ our true sav-iour: hear the ca-rol___ that we sing you, and the tid-ings___ that we

2 There the vir-gin___ mo-ther Ma-ry tends her in-fant =___ oh so gen-tly; and the beau-ty___ of the God-head shines a-round him =___ her be-

3 Let the might-y___ faint and trem-ble at the tri-umph___ of the hum-ble; and the guil-ty___ leave their sigh-ing where the sin-ner's___ hope is

This lovely Spanish carol requries both rhythmic vitality and a certain gentleness in performance. It is very effective if the chorus is sung in harmony.

36 IN SILENT STILLNESS

PAKISTAN

Words: from Psalm 62
translated from the Punjabi
by Alison Fookes
Music: unknown
arranged Geoff Weaver

Confidently ♩. = 68

Chorus

In si - lent still-ness, wait for God and rest, my soul, in peace:____ in

last time **to Coda** ⊕

him your hopes will be ful-filled your fears will find re -

Verse

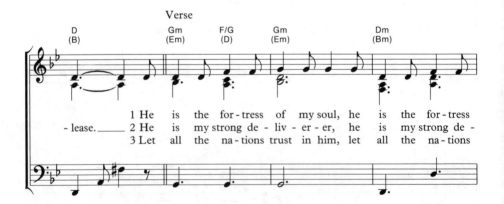

1 He is the for-tress of my soul, he is the for-tress
- lease.____ 2 He is my strong de - liv - er - er, he is my strong de -
3 Let all the na-tions trust in him, let all the na-tions

This expressive Punjabi setting of words from Psalm 62 is sung by Pakistani Christians who are a very small minority in an Islamic state. Although in the minor key, it should be sung with rhythm and conviction. When changing from § to ⅜, the speed of the dotted crotchet is equal to the crotchet of the new pattern.

37 ISA MASIH
Jesus the Lord is seeking me

PAKISTAN

Words: translated from the original
by Alison Fookes
Music: unknown

Unhurried ♩. = 48

I - sa ma - sih ma la - ta - vi ma da gu - nah na tcha

Chorus

la - sa - vi. Je - sus the Lord is seek - ing me,

Fine Verse

and from my sin he will set me free.
1 Who is the one who
2 Why does he care so
3 This is the rea - son –

D.S.

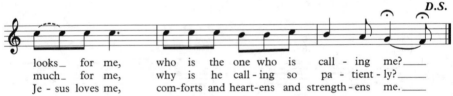

looks_ for me, who is the one who is call - ing me?____
much_ for me, why is he call - ing so pa - tient - ly?____
Je - sus loves me, com - forts and heart - ens and strength - ens me.____

4 How can he give such comfort to me –
   there is such weakness and sin in me.
      Jesus the Lord . . .

5 He gave his life in sacrifice
   and for my sin he has paid the price.
      Jesus the Lord . . .

6 I am so glad he set me free –
   I'll live with God for eternity.
      Jesus the Lord . . .

> This haunting song comes from the North-West Frontier province of Pakistan,
> and is best sung unaccompanied. Christians in Pakistan are in a small minority. It
> is good that we remember them and identify with them as we sing this song.

JESU TAWA PANO
Jesus we are here

ZIMBABWE

Words and music: Patrick Matsikenyiri

With expression ♩ = 100

Je - su ta - wa pa - no; Je - su
Je - sus, we are here;__ Je - sus,

ta - wa pa - no; Je - su ta - wa pa - no;
we are here;__ Je - sus, we are here;__

(except last time) *Mam - bo Je - su.*

ta - wa pa - no mu zi - ta re - nyu.
we are here_____ for_____ you.

A gathering song, originally from Shona, and composed by Patrick Matsikenyiri, a primary school headmaster and a leading composer of African Church music. The harmonic clash in bar five is deliberate. Patrick said to John Bell of the Iona Community, 'If you knew the history of our country, you would know that we have had so many clashes that a little difficulty in the harmony will cause us no problem'. Other verses may be added e.g. We are here *with* you, . . . *in* you.

39 JESUS, JESUS, HOW I ADORE YOU
Jai, Jai, Yisu

Words: after C. D. Rockley
and in this version Word & Music
Music: Hindustani melody
arranged Geoff Weaver

Je - sus, Je - sus, how I a - dore____ you,

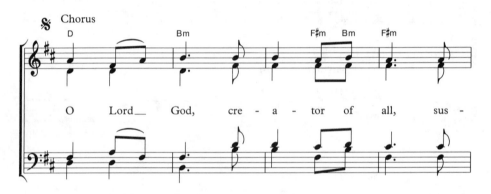

Chorus

O Lord____ God, cre - a - tor of all, sus -

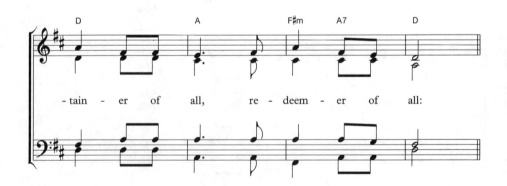

-tain - er of all, re - deem - er of all:

> An earthy rhythmical refrain which is based on an Hindustani folk melody, and has
> something of the character of a folk dance. The verse should be more delicate in style.

Fine

Je - sus, Je - sus, how I a - dore___ you!

SOLO

1 Leav - ing your glo - ry with love your great de - sign,_____
2 When I____ come to____ you____ in my pain_____
3 Al - le - lu - ia;____ glo - ry,____ glo - ry;____

giv - ing your life and____ so re - deem - ing mine;____
you give____ me your____ peace____ once a - gain;____
Ev - ery - bo - dy,____ tell____ the____ sto - ry,

1st time SOLO
2nd time ALL PARTS

D.S. al Fine

O Lord Je - sus, come; O Joy - giv - er come;
Re - liev - ing____ my load, guid - ing my road;
Come one, come____ all, come heed God's____ call;

40 JESUS THE LORD SAID

INDIA

Words: anonymous
translated Dermott Monahan
Music: Urdu melody
arranged Geoff Weaver

Steadily ♩ = 88

1 Je - sus the Lord said: 'I am the Bread, the Bread of___ Life_ for the
2 Je - sus the Lord said: 'I am the Door, the Way and the Door for the
3 Je - sus the Lord said: 'I am the Light, the one true_ Light of the

world am I. The Bread of___ Life_ for the world am I, the
poor am I. The Way and the Door for the poor am I, the
world am I. The one true_ Light of the world am I, the

Bread of___ Life_ for the world am I'. Je - sus the Lord said:
Way and the Door for the poor am I'. Je - sus the Lord said:
one true_ Light of the world am I'. Je - sus the Lord said:

One of the most widely travelled of Indian hymns, this haunting melody
is Urdu in origin. It makes an ideal vehicle through which to teach many
of Jesus' sayings about himself, and maybe expand it ad lib.

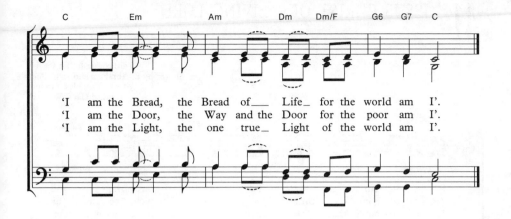

'I am the Bread, the Bread of__ Life_ for the world am I'.
'I am the Door, the Way and the Door for the poor am I'.
'I am the Light, the one true_ Light of the world am I'.

1 Jesus the Lord said: 'I am the Bread,
  the Bread of Life for the world am I.
    The Bread of Life for the world am I,
    the Bread of Life for the world am I'.
  Jesus the Lord said: 'I am the Bread,
  the Bread of Life for the world am I'.

2 Jesus the Lord said: 'I am the Door,
  the Way and the Door for the poor am I' . . .

3 Jesus the Lord said: 'I am the Light,
  the one true Light of the world am I' . . .

4 Jesus the Lord said: 'I am the Shepherd,
  the one Good Shepherd of the sheep am I' . . .

5 Jesus the Lord said: 'I am the Life,
  the Resurrection and the Life am I' . . .

41 JESUS CHRIST OUR LIVING LORD

HUNGARY

Words: after E. Turmezei
translated by E. Abraham and John Bell
Music: Szokolay Sandor
arranged Geoff Weaver

Steadily ♩ = 76

1 Je - sus Christ, our liv - ing__ Lord, we be - lieve you
2 In the humbl-est things we__ do we'll ac - count our -
3 Food e - nough that all may__ feed, grace e - nough for
4 Lord in all we do to - day let our lives pre -

keep your__ word:__ what - ev - er may be - fall us,
- selves to__ you;__ mak - ing your love our mea - sure,
each one's__ need = even as we praise you, sing - ing
- pare your__ way;__ may peace and love be - friend us

stretch or stall__ us, we'll trust your__ voice to call us.
truth and trea - sure, your will our__ joy and plea - sure.
you come bring - ing gifts at the__ day's be - gin - ning.
and de - fend__ us wher - ev - er__ you may send us.

> Folk-song like in character, this hymn was published in a new hymnbook
> produced in 1981 by the Hungarian Ecumenical Council of Churches.

42 KAY YAHWEH AKO

I'll follow my Lord

PHILIPPINES

Words: from the Tagalog
in this version Word & Music
Music: unknown
arranged Geoff Weaver

Relaxed, easy flow ♩ = 88

Kay Yah-weh a - ko, kay Yah-weh a - ko Kay
I'll fol-low my Lord, I'll fol-low my Lord, I'll

Yah-weh a - ko ma - na - na-na - gan Kay
fol-low my Lord — to Je - sus I cling; I'll

Yah-weh a - ko, kay Yah-weh a - ko, Kay
fol-low my Lord, I'll fol-low my Lord, I'll

Yah-weh a - ko ma - na - na-gan.
fol-low my Lord — my love I will bring!

The arranger heard this beautiful song sung by Filipino Christians who had
recently suffered devastation from earthquake, volcanic eruption and typhoon.
In that context, to sing, 'to Jesus I cling', has tremendous power and relevance. Its folk-song character is well served by a guitar accompaniment.

43 KHUDAYA, RAHEM KAR
Have mercy on us, Lord

PAKISTAN

KYRIE

Words: traditional
Music: traditional Urdu
arranged Geoff Weaver

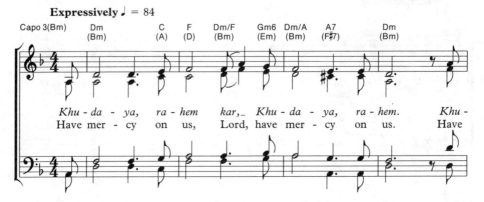

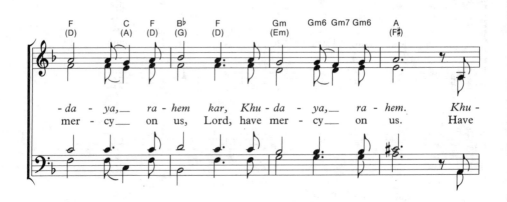

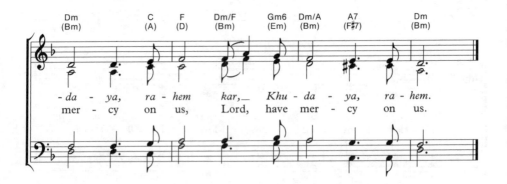

This expressive Kyrie was sung at the WCC Seventh Assembly in Canberra in 1991. The Indian subcontinent is often devastated by natural disasters and this plea for mercy may be sung both in a personal and a corporate sense.

44 KYRIE ELEISON
Lord have mercy

C.I.S.

KYRIE

Words: traditional
Music: traditional Russian Orthodox

Slowly ♩ = 60

Ky - ri - e   e - lei - son.   Ky - ri - e   e - lei - son.
Lord,____ have mer - cy.   Lord,____ have mer - cy.

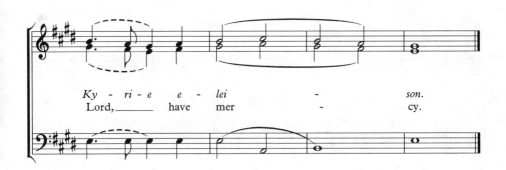

Ky - ri - e   e - lei   -   son.
Lord,____ have mer   -   cy.

Kyrie eleison.
Kyrie eleison.
Kyrie eleison.

Lord, have mercy.
Lord, have mercy.
Lord, have mercy.

Originally from the Russian Orthodox Church, this simple chant is ideal for encouraging a congregation to sing in harmony. It may be used repeatedly as a focus for meditation.

45 KYRIE ELEISON
Lord have mercy

GHANA

Words: traditional
Music: Dinah Reindorf
arranged Geoff Weaver

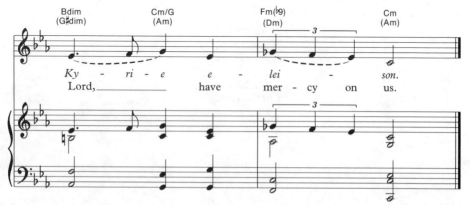

It is not too fanciful to hear in this expressive Kyrie, with echoes of the blues in its final phrase, so much of the pain and suffering of Ghana's colonial past with its slave trade and enforced break-up of families. Dinah Reindorf, one of Ghana's leading musicians, composed this in response to a Passion Walk, walking in Christ's footsteps to the cross.

46 LORD, AS I WAKE I TURN TO YOU

IRELAND

Words: Brian Foley
Music: Irish traditional melody
arranged Geoff Weaver

1 Lord, as I wake I turn to you, ____ your-self the first thought of my day; ____ my king, my God, whose help is sure, ____ your-self the help for which I pray.

2 There is no bless - ing, Lord, from you ____ for those who make their will their way, ____ no praise for those who will not praise, ____ no peace for those who will not pray.

3 Your lov - ing gifts of grace to me, ____ those fav - ours I could ne - ver earn, ____ call for my thanks in ____ praise and prayer, ____ call me to love you in re - turn.

4 Lord, make my life a life of love, ____ keep me from sin in all I do; ____ Lord, make your law ____ my ____ on - ly law, ____ your will my will, for love of you.

A little known and haunting Irish melody
provides an appropriate setting of Psalm 5.

47 LET MY SPIRIT REJOICE IN YOUR LOVE

PAKISTAN

Words: from the Urdu
Alison Fookes
Music: unknown
arranged Geoff Weaver

An Urdu song which somehow combines a minor mode and an expression of real joy.
It should move quite quickly. The chorus may be sung by all, while the verse should be solo.

48 LOOK AND LEARN

KOREA

Words: from Matthew 6: 23–34
John Bell
Music: Nah Young-Soo
arranged Geoff Weaver

1 Look and learn from the birds of the air, fly-ing high a-bove
2 Look and learn from the flowers of the field, bring-ing beau-ty and
3 What God wants should be our will; where God calls should

wor-ry and fear; nei-ther sow-ing or har-vest-ing seed,
col-our to life; nei-ther sew-ing nor tail-or-ing cloth,
be our goal. When we seek the King-dom first,

yet they're gi-ven what-ev-er they need. If the God of
yet they're dressed in the fin-est at-tire. If the God of
all we've lost is ours a-gain. Let's be done with

On hearing this haunting pentatonic melody, many people are surprised to learn
of its Korean origin. This should have an easy flow, not moving too slowly.

earth and heaven cares for birds as much__ as this,
earth and heaven cares for flowers as much__ as this,
anx - ious thoughts, set a - side to - mor - row's cares,

won't he care much more for you,
won't he care much more for you
live each day__ that God pro-vides

if you put_ your trust_ in him?
if you put_ your trust_ in him?
put-ting all__ our trust_ in him.

1 Look and learn from the birds of the air,
flying high above worry and fear;
neither sowing or harvesting seed,
yet they're given whatever they need.
If the God of earth and heaven
cares for birds as much as this,
won't he care much more for you,
if you put your trust in him?

2 Look and learn from the flowers of the field,
bringing beauty and colour to life;
neither sewing nor tailoring cloth,
yet they're dressed in the finest attire.
If the God of earth and heaven
cares for flowers as much as this,
won't he care much more for you
if you put your trust in him?

3 What God wants should be our will;
where God calls should be our goal.
When we seek the Kingdom first,
all we've lost is ours again.
Let's be done with anxious thoughts,
set aside tomorrow's cares,
live each day that God provides
putting all our trust in him.

49 LORD, FORGIVE ME

Words: Ellsworth Candlee
Music: Confucian Chant
arranged Geoff Weaver

♩ = 92

ORGAN PEDAL

1 Lord, for - give__ me. Christ, have mer - cy!
2 Lord, for - give__ me. Christ, have mer - cy!

I con - fess to you all my sin and shame.
Now to turn from sin, Lord, grant heaven - ly grace.

Save me, Lord, I cry. In your cross I trust,
Raised up and re - newed, may I fol - low you,

In the early 20th century, it was often said in China 'One Christian more means one Chinese less.' The use of an ancient Confucian chant in worship is one way in which Chinese Christians are able to root their faith in their Chinese culture and traditions.

Je - sus, Son of God, ho - ly, bless - ed one.
Je - sus, Son of God, ho - ly, bless - ed one.

1 Lord, forgive me. Christ, have mercy!
I confess to you all my sin and shame.
Save me, Lord, I cry.
In your cross I trust,
Jesus, Son of God, holy, blessed one.

2 Lord, forgive me. Christ, have mercy!
Now to turn from sin, Lord,
grant heavenly grace.
Raised up and renewed, may I follow you,
Jesus, Son of God, holy, blessed one.

50 MAYENZIWE 'NTANDO YAKHO

Your will be done on earth

SOUTH AFRICA

Words: from the Lord's Prayer
Music: traditional
transcribed by John Bell

Not too fast

Ma - ye - nzi - we_____ 'nta -
Your will be done_____ on

Ma - ye - nzi - we_____ 'nta -
Your will be done_____ on

- ndo ya - kho. Ma - ye - nzi - we_____ 'nta -
earth, O Lord. Your will be done__ on

- ndo ya - kho. Ma - ye - nzi - we_____ 'nta -
earth, O Lord. Your will be done__ on

- ndo ya - kho. Ma - ye - nzi - we_____ 'nta -
earth, O Lord. Your will__ be done__ on

A traditional song from South Africa, joyful
and affirmative. This is best sung a cappella.

- ndo___ ya - kho.___ Ma - ye - nzi - we 'nta - ndo ya
earth,_ O Lord._ Your will be done on earth, O

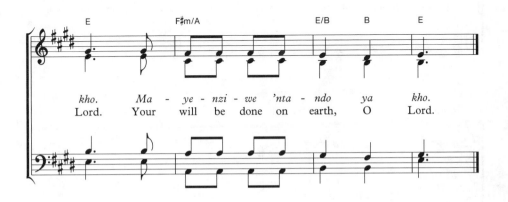

kho. Ma - ye - nzi - we 'nta - ndo ya kho.
Lord. Your will be done on earth, O Lord.

Mayenziwe 'ntando yakho.
Mayenziwe 'ntando yakho.
Mayenziwe 'ntando yakho.
Mayenziwe 'ntando yakho.
Mayenziwe 'ntando yakho.

Your will be done on earth, O Lord.
Your will be done on earth, O Lord.
Your will be done on earth, O Lord.
Your will be done on earth, O Lord.
Your will be done on earth, O Lord.

51 MFURAHINI, HALLELUYA
He has arisen, alleluia!

TANZANIA

Words: Bernard Kyamanywa
Howard S. Olson
Music: traditional
arranged Geoff Weaver

Verse SOLO

1 M - fu - ra - hi - ni, hal - le - lu - ya m - ko - mbo - zi a - me - fu - fu - ka. A - me - fu - fu - ka, hal - le - lu - ya. M - si - fu - ni sa - sa yu ha - i.

2 A - me - fu - fu - ka M - ko - mbo - zi hal - le - lu - ya, tu - sha - ngi - li - e. Ngu - vu za mwo - vu a - me - shi - nda. A - me - tu - on - do - a ku - fa - ni.

1 He has a - ris - en, al - le - lu - ia! Re - joice and praise him, al - le - lu - ia! For our Re - deem - er burst from the tomb — e - ven from death, dis - pell - ing its gloom.

2 For three long days the grave did its worst un - til its strength by God was dis - persed. He who gives life did death un - der - go, and in its con - quest his might did show.

A traditional dance-like Tanzanian song which needs to move at a lively one in a bar. The leader-congregation format is typically African. The song would be enhanced by appropriate drum rhythms.

Words: African Bernard Kyamanywa
English © Howard Olson, Lutheran World Federation

Music arrangement: © 1993 Geoff Weaver / Jubilee Hymns

Chorus ALL (HARMONY)

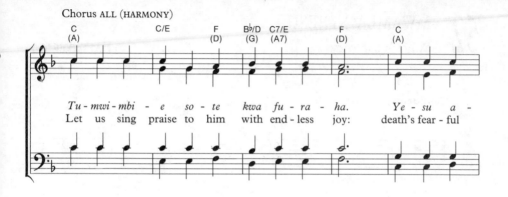

Tu - mwi - mbi - e so - te kwa fu - ra - ha. Ye - su a -
Let us sing praise to him with end - less joy: death's fear - ful

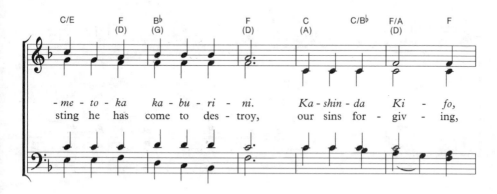

- me - to - ka ka - bu - ri - ni. Ka - shin - da Ki - fo,
sting he has come to des - troy, our sins for - giv - ing,

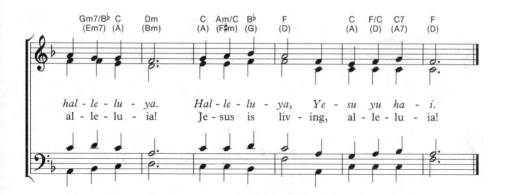

hal - le - lu - ya. Hal - le - lu - ya, Ye - su yu ha - i.
al - le - lu - ia! Je - sus is liv - ing, al - le - lu - ia!

3 *Malaika aliwaambia*
   wanawake, 'Msiogope.
   Sasa kaburi lipo tupu
   kwani Yesu amefufuka.'
   Tumwimbie sote . . .

4 *'Amebatilisha Shetani.*
   Amewaletea wokovu.
   Kwa hiyo ninyi mtangaze
   ni hakika, Yesu yu hai.'
   Tumwimbie sote . . .

3 The angel said to them, 'Do not fear
   you look for Jesus – he is not here.
   See for yourselves, the tomb is all bare,
   only the grave-clothes are lying there.'
   Let us sing . . .

4 Go spread the news, he's not in the grave:
   he has arisen, mighty to save.
   Jesus' redeeming labours are done –
   even the battle with sin is won.
   Let us sing . . .

52 MWAMBA NI JESU
Who is the rock

EAST AFRICA

Words and music: unknown

A song in the African call-response tradition. No books are required for the congregation and the song can be extended indefinitely as the soloist recalls the different attributes of Jesus the Rock.

1 SOLO *Mwamba, Mwamba?*
  ALL *Mwamba ni Jesu, Mwamba.*
  SOLO *Mwamba, Mwamba?*
  ALL *Mwamba ni Jesu, Mwamba.*

2 SOLO *Abariki:*
  ALL *Mwamba ni Jesu, Mwamba.*
  SOLO *Abariki:*
  ALL *Mwamba ni Jesu, Mwamba.*

3 SOLO *Anaponya:*
  ALL *Mwamba ni Jesu, Mwamba.*
  SOLO *Anaponya:*
  ALL *Mwamba ni Jesu, Mwamba.*

4 SOLO *Analinda:*
  ALL *Mwamba ni Jesu, Mwamba.*
  SOLO *Analinda:*
  ALL *Mwamba ni Jesu, Mwamba.*

5 SOLO *Aokoa:*
  ALL *Mwamba ni Jesu, Mwamba.*
  SOLO *Aokoa:*
  ALL *Mwamba ni Jesu, Mwamba.*

6 SOLO *Mwamba . . .*

7 SOLO *Mwamba . . .*

1 SOLO Who is the Rock?
  ALL The Rock is Jesus, the Rock.
  SOLO Who is the Rock?
  ALL The Rock is Jesus, the Rock.

2 SOLO He blesses us:
  ALL the Rock is Jesus, the Rock.
  SOLO He blesses us:
  ALL the Rock is Jesus, the Rock.

3 SOLO He heals from sin:
  ALL The Rock is Jesus, the Rock.
  SOLO He heals from sin:
  ALL The Rock is Jesus, the Rock.

4 SOLO The Rock protects:
  ALL The Rock is Jesus, the Rock.
  SOLO The Rock protects:
  ALL The Rock is Jesus, the Rock.

5 SOLO He rescues us:
  ALL The Rock is Jesus, the Rock.
  SOLO He rescues us:
  ALL The Rock is Jesus, the Rock.

6 SOLO Who is the Rock . . .

7 SOLO Who is the Rock . . .

53 MOTO UMEWAKA LEO
God's fire

EAST AFRICA

Words and music: unknown
arranged Geoff Weaver

Lively ♩ = 108

Mo - to u - me-wa-ka le - o, Mo - to ni
God's fire is burn-ing in my soul, God's fire has

ka - zi ya Ye - su, Mo - to u - me - wa - ka le - o; Tu -
come to make me whole, God's fire is sweep-ing through the earth; praise

-im - be hal - le - lu - jah___ mo - to u - me - wa - ka! Tu -
God, I've got God's fire and___ it's burn-ing in my soul! Praise

-im - be hal - le - lu - jah___ mo - to u - me - wa - ka!
God – yes, hal - le - lu - jah___ it's burn-ing in my soul!

A song which most probably came out of the East African revival.
It needs to be sung with rhythm, fire and commitment.

Music arrangement: © 1993 Geoff Weaver / Jubilate Hymns   Words: African and English Copyright control

54 MY PRAYERS RISE

Uknown

Words: from Psalm 141: 2
Arlo D. Buba
Music: Arlo D. Buba
arranged Geoff Weaver

Meditatively ♩ = 88

My prayers rise like___ in - cense, my

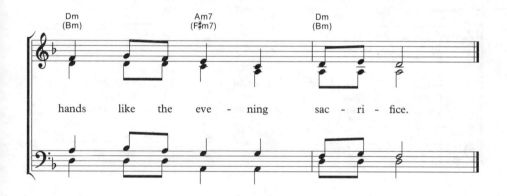

hands like the eve - ning sac - ri - fice.

My prayers rise like incense,
my hands like the evening sacrifice.

This simple response was first sung as part of a service for justice, peace and
the integrity of creation. It can be used effectively within a time of prayer.

55 MY SOUL WILL GLORIFY

INDONESIA

Words: from Luke 1
D. T. Niles
Music: Maluku popular song
arranged Geoff Weaver

Dance like ♩. = 72

1 My soul will glo-ri-fy the Lord my spi-rit will__ re-
2 Re-joice for ev-er at my name, for God has done__ great
3 The proud he scat-ters in their pride, the rich must emp-ty

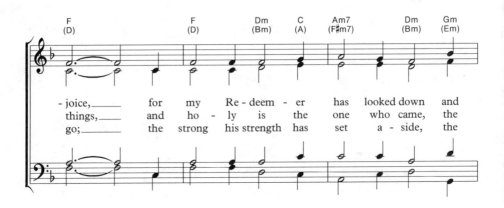

-joice,__ for my Re-deem-er has looked down and
things,__ and ho-ly is the one who came, the
go;__ the strong his strength has set a-side, the

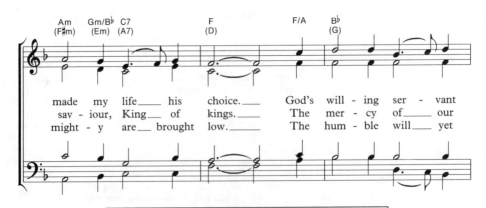

made my life__ his choice.__ God's will-ing ser-vant
sav-iour, King__ of kings.__ The mer-cy of__ our
might-y are__ brought low.__ The hum-ble will__ yet

This captures beautifully the joy and the dance-like character
of Mary's song. Ideally it should be sung unaccompanied.

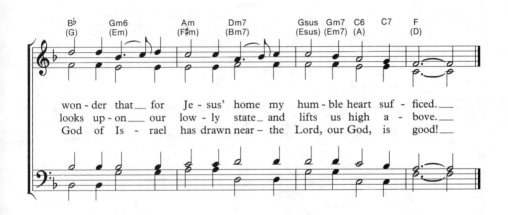

1   My soul will glorify the Lord
my spirit will rejoice,
for my Redeemer has looked down
and made my life his choice.
God's willing servant I'll become –
the mother of the Christ,
and wonder that for Jesus' home
my humble heart sufficed.

2   Rejoice for ever at my name,
for God has done great things,
and holy is the one who came,
the saviour, King of kings.
The mercy of our God is great,
and sure his deeds of love;
he looks upon our lowly state
and lifts us high above.

3   The proud he scatters in their pride,
the rich must empty go;
the strong his strength has set aside,
the mighty are brought low.
The humble will yet high appear,
the poor be filled with food;
the God of Israel has drawn near –
the Lord, our God, is good!

56 NA JIJOHO
Peace be with you

BENIN

Words: traditional
Music: unknown
arranged Geoff Weaver

Confidently ♩ = 104

D   A7   D

SOLO
Na Ji-jo-ho,   *ji - jo-ho ni   tin.*   *Na Ji-jo-ho.*
Peace be with you,   peace   be___ with   you.   Peace be with you,

D   A7   D   D/F♯   G   A

ALL
ji - jo-ho ni   tin.   Po___   ome - po - po,   A -
peace   be___ with   you,   with_ all   of___   us,   A -
ome - po - po,   A -
all of us,   A -

D   D/F♯   G   A   D

- men.   Po___   ome - po -   po,   A -   men!
- men,   with_ all   of___   us,   A -   men!
- men   ome - po - po,   A -   men!
- men   all   of   us,   A -   men!

> This song is very popular in Benin and is sung at thanksgiving and indeed on almost
> any occasion. It is simple enough to sing as greetings, or as *the Peace* is exchanged.

57 NGARIKUDZWE ZUVA
Come let us celebrate the day

ZIMBABWE

Words: from the Zimbabwe
in this version Word & Music
Music: Abraham Maraire

Exuberantly ♩. = 125

Verse

1 Nag - ri - ku-dzwe zu - va i - ro a - no-mu - ka.
2 Ru - fa - ro ku - ne ma - ko - re___ a - ke.
3 Kri - si - tu zvi-sho - ma kwa - ti - ri wa-pi - wa.
4 Zvi - no u - no-pi - nda ma - te-nga ku-mu-so - ro.

1 Come let us ce - le - brate the day of Je-sus' ri - sing.
2 For he has re - con - ciled us to___ the___ Fa - ther.
3 To earth he came in love to be___ our___ bro - ther.
4 Now high - ex - al - ted he is yet___ a - mong us.

Chorus

Ha - le - lu - ja,___ ha - le - lu - ja!
Hal - le - lu - jah,___ hal - le - lu - jah!

Final Chorus

Ha - le - lu - ja,___ ha - le - lu - ja,
Hal - le - lu - jah,___ hal - le - lu - jah,

- lu - ja, - lu - ja, ha - le - lu - ja,___ ha - le - lu - ja!
- lu-jah, - lu-jah, hal-le - lu - jah,___ hal - le - lu-jah!

An exuberant Easter song which is enhanced by rhythmic accompaniment as follows:

Verse ‖: ♪♪♪ ♪♪♪ ♪♪ ♪♪ :‖   First Chorus ‖: ♩ ♩ ♩ ♪♩ ♪♪ :‖

Final Chorus ‖: ♩ ♪♩♩ ♩ ♪♩ :‖

The final chorus can be taken out of context and used in a variety of ways.

58 NANTI ITHEMBA
God sent his son

ZIMBABWE

Words: from the African
Geoff Weaver
Music: unknown
arranged Joseph Kiwele

Lively

Verse

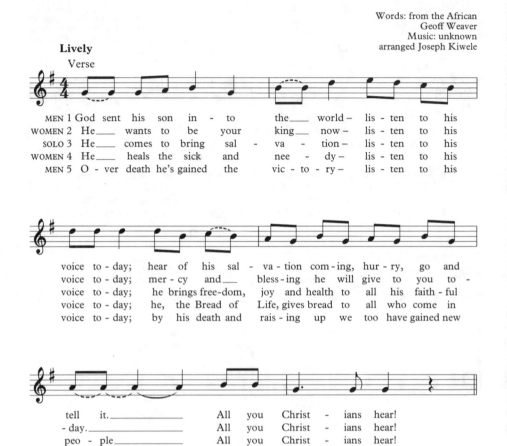

MEN 1 God sent his son in - to the___ world – lis - ten to his
WOMEN 2 He___ wants to be your king___ now – lis - ten to his
SOLO 3 He___ comes to bring sal - va - tion – lis - ten to his
WOMEN 4 He___ heals the sick and nee - dy – lis - ten to his
MEN 5 O - ver death he's gained the vic - to - ry – lis - ten to his

voice to - day; hear of his sal - va - tion com - ing, hur - ry, go and
voice to - day; mer - cy and___ bless - ing he will give to you to -
voice to - day; he brings free - dom, joy and health to all his faith - ful
voice to - day; he, the Bread of Life, gives bread to all who come in
voice to - day; by his death and rais - ing up we too have gained new

tell it.___ All you Christ - ians hear!
- day.___ All you Christ - ians hear!
peo - ple___ All you Christ - ians hear!
need.___ All you Christ - ians hear!
life to - day.___ All you Christ - ians hear!

Chorus

ALL Sing hal - le - lu - jah, night is gone;___ let us re-joice the

Sing hal - le - lu - jah, night is gone;___

An exuberant Advent or Christmas song from Zimbabwe.
It should be unaccompanied and with lively drum accompaniment.

morn-ing comes,___ Christ has come and he is here.___ Hal-le - lu-jah!

let us re-joice the morn-ing comes,___ Hal-le - lu-jah!

1 MEN   God sent his son into the world –
          listen to his voice today;
          hear of his salvation coming, hurry, go and tell it.
          All you Christians hear!

   ALL   Sing hallelujah, night is gone;
          let us rejoice the morning comes,
          Christ has come and he is here.
          Hallelujah!

2 WOMEN He wants to be your king now –
          listen to his voice today;
          mercy and blessing
             he will give you today.
          All you Christians hear!

   ALL   Sing hallelujah, night is gone . . .

3 SOLO   He comes to bring salvation –
          listen to his voice today;
          he brings freedom, joy and health
             to all his faithful people
          All you Christians hear!

   ALL   Sing hallelujah, night is gone . . .

4 WOMEN He heals the sick and needy –
          listen to his voice today;
          he, the Bread of Life, gives
             bread to all who come in need.
          All you Christians hear!

   ALL   Sing hallelujah, night is gone . . .

5 MEN   Over death he's gained the victory –
          listen to his voice today;
          by his death and raising up
             we too have gained new life today.
          All you Christians hear!

   ALL   Sing hallelujah, night is gone . . .

NGAIH CHIAT TAHNAK KA TON LID AH

When I am sad and sorrowful

MYANMAR

Words: unknown
in this version Word & Music
Music: unknown
arranged David Peacock

Lilting ♩ = 108

Ngaih chiat tah - nak   ka ton lid ah,   a ka hnum   tu
When I am sad and sor - row - ful,   Je - sus is   there;

hawi tha bik   cu   Je - suh   a   si___
he's my best friend, my   Sa -   viour.___

dwat mi hna nih thlan mual ran - liam   lid can zon - gah
When all my friends have gone a - way,   in that sad   day,

bawi Je - suh   nih   a   ka um - pi.___
Je - sus my Lord   is   with___ me.___   More

The recent history of Myanmar (Burma) has been one of great oppression and suffering. The editor recently met a young man who dared not return home to his family and this song was sung to him by another radical young Christian who feared for the future of his country. Many families have lost loved ones and the words of this song must be truly heartfelt.

60 ODI, ODI
We're told he was born at a Bethlehem inn

ZIMBABWE

Words: from Zimbabwe
Geoff Weaver, in this version Word & Music
Music: unknown
arranged Geoff Weaver

Brightly ♩. = 60

Capo 3(D)   Verse

UNISON 1 We're told he was born at a Beth-le-hem inn, where
HARMONY 2 He comes now — a stran-ger who asks for our aid, he
HARMONY 4 He comes as a bro-ther, he comes as a friend, he
UNISON 5 Lord Je-sus, you're wel-come, the door's o-pen wide; we

Jo-seph and Ma-ry had begged to get in; for birth-place a sta-ble was
comes in dis-guise that he might per-suade; he comes to us ear-ly, he
comes all our ha-tred and war-fare to end; he comes to u-nite and he
beg you to en-ter and with us a-bide: your love in our heart and your

all they could find al-though he was God's gift to all of our kind.
comes to us late, and hum-bly he waits and he cries at our gate.
comes to re-store, but — al-ways so hum-bly — he calls at our door.
smile on our face, we'll see you in stran-gers who stand in your place.

Chorus
v.1 UNISON MEN
vv.2,3,4 HARMONY

'O - di, o - di!' a stran-ger has come! 'O -

'Odi' means 'hello'. The harmonies are best realised a cappella and
a single drum beat helps to maintain a gentle two in a bar feel. This
arrangement gives opportunity for plenty of textural variety.

last time **to Coda** ⊕

Verse 3 _lower parts hum_

-di, o - di! Will you wel-come me here?' 'O - di, o - di! I

stand here and wait.' 'O - di, o - di! Will you o - pen your gate?'

3 He comes as a ser - vant to black and to white, and

shows us the way that we all may u - nite; he of - fers his friend-ship to

61 OH, ISN'T IT GOOD
Perfect harmony

BLACK GOSPEL

Words and music: Howard Francis
and Wayne Wilson

Oh, is-n't it good_ to be as one,_ liv-ing in per - fect har-mo-ny,

_ shar - ing the good_ things_ God_ has done, God_ has done?_

Coming from a Black Gospel tradition, this ecstatic song requires
rhythmic freedom and a wide range of emotional expression.

Chorus

Oh, is-n't it good_ to be as one,___ liv-ing in per-

-fect har-mo-ny,___ shar-ing the good___ things God

repeat chorus ad lib.

_ has done,_ God___ has done?___ Ooh.

62 OUR FATHER WHO IS IN HEAVEN

CARIBBEAN

Words: Lord's Prayer
Music: unknown
arranged David Peacock

This well known Caribbean setting of the Lord's Prayer can be sung very effectively as a solo-response song, with the congregation singing the refrain 'Hallowed by your name', preferably in simple harmonies as suggested.

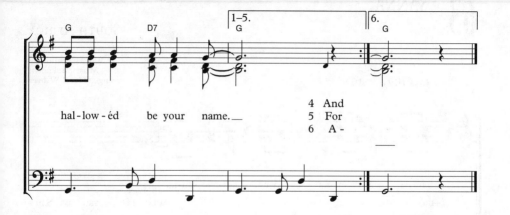

hal-low-éd   be your   name.___   4 And
                                       5 For
                                       6 A -

1   Our Father who is in heaven,
    hallowéd be your name,
    your kingdom come, your will be done,
    hallowéd be your name.

2   On earth as it is in heaven,
    hallowéd be your name,
    give us this day our daily bread,
    hallowéd be your name.

3   Forgive us all our trespasses,
    hallowéd be your name,
    as we forgive those who trespass against us,
    hallowéd be your name.

4   And lead us not into temptation,
    hallowéd be your name,
    but deliver us from all that is evil,
    hallowéd be your name.

5   For yours is the kingdom, the power and the glory,
    hallowéd be your name,
    for ever and for ever,
    hallowéd be your name.

6   Amen, amen, amen, amen,
    hallowéd be your name,
    amen, amen, amen, amen,
    hallowéd be your name.

63 SANNA

SOUTH AFRICA

Words: traditional
Music: unknown
arranged Geoff Weaver

Joyfully ♩ = 100

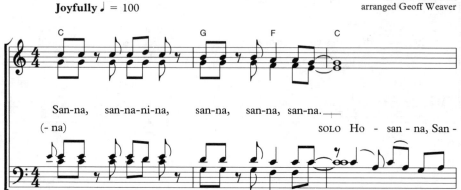

San-na, san-na-ni-na, san-na, san-na, san-na.___
(- na)
SOLO Ho - san - na, San-

San-na, san-na-ni-na, san-na, san-na, san-na.___ San -
SOLO Ho - san - na

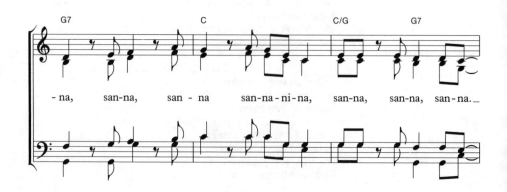

- na, san-na, san - na san-na-ni-na, san-na, san-na, san-na._

> *Sanna* is a shortened form of *Hosanna*. It is very effective to start this
> song quietly, as if in a distant procession, and then to get louder and
> more exuberant as the imaginary procession draws nearer.

Sanna, sanna, sanna san-na-ni-na,
SOLO Ho - san - na

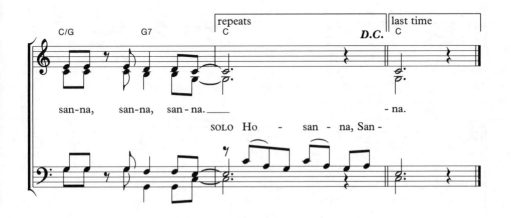

san-na, san-na, san - na.____ - na.
SOLO Ho - san - na, San-

Sanna, sanna-nina,
sanna, sanna, sanna.
Sanna, sanna-nina,
sanna, sanna, sanna.

Sanna, sanna, sanna
sannanina,
sanna, sanna, sanna.
Sanna, sanna, sanna
sannanina,
sanna, sanna, sanna.

64 SANTO, SANTO
Holy, holy

ARGENTINA

Words and music: unknown
arranged Geoff Weaver

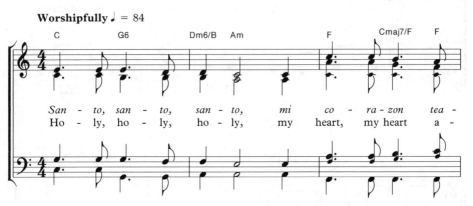

Worshipfully ♩ = 84

San - to, san - to, san - to, mi co - ra - zon tea -
Ho - ly, ho - ly, ho - ly, my heart, my heart a -

- do - ra! Mi co - ra zon te
- dores you! My heart is glad to

sabe de - cir: san - to eres Se - ñor.
say the_ words: you are ho - ly, Lord.

> This heart-felt love song may be sung in
> unison, in two parts, or in rich harmony.

Santo, santo, santo,
mi corazon te adora!
Mi corazon te sabe decir:
santo eres Señor.

Holy, holy, holy,
my heart, my heart adores you!
My heart is glad to say the words:
you are holy, Lord.

INSTRUMENTAL OBLIGATO

Oboe

Flute

Clarinet

Simple part

65 SANTO, SANTO, SANTO
Holy, holy, holy is the Lord

EL SALVADOR

Words: unknown
English adaptation, Word & Music
Music: unknown
arranged Christopher Norton

San-to, san - to, san - to, san - to, san-to,
Ho-ly, ho - ly, ho - ly, ho - ly, ho-ly,

san - toes nues - tro Dios, Se - ñor de to - da la tie - rra, san-to,
ho - ly is our God; God, the Lord of earth and hea - ven, holy,

san - toes nues - tro Dios. San-to, san - to, san - to, san - to, san-to,
ho - ly is our God. Ho-ly, ho - ly, ho - ly, ho - ly, ho-ly,

This extract from the Misa Popular Salvadorena, with its characteristic folk dance alternation of § and ¾ time, needs a lively rhythmic accompaniment (percussion and guitars) and a radiant abandon on the part of the congregation.

66 SENHOR, TEM PIEDADE DE NÓS

O Lord, have mercy on us

BRAZIL

KYRIE

Music: Jaci Maraschin
arranged David Peacock

Underlying this wonderful Brazilian setting of the Kyrie, are the rhythms of the dance. The melodic line should be smooth, the accompaniment much less so.

67 SENT BY THE LORD AM I

NICARAGUA

Words: from the oral tradition
translation Jorge Maldonodo
Music: traditional
arranged David Peacock

A song from the folk tradition of Nicaragua. The use of the minor key somehow adds strength and resolve to the commitment to Christ's mission.

Music arrangement: © 1993 David Peacock / Jubilee Hymns

Words: translation © 1991 Jorge Maldonodo / World Council of Churches, Geneva

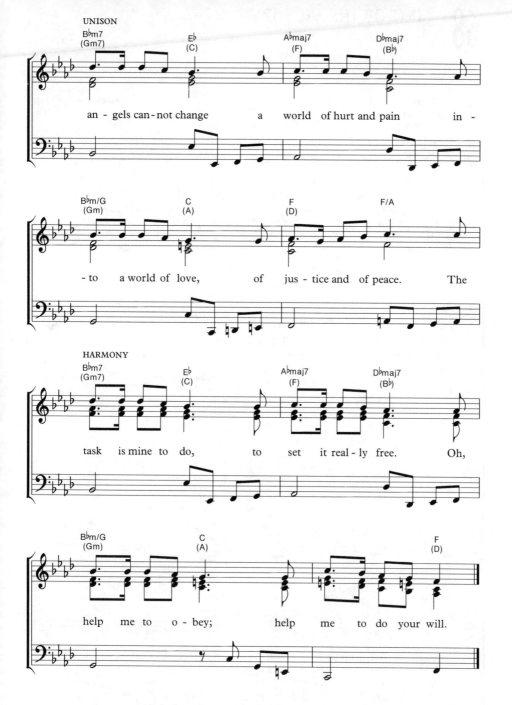

Sent by the Lord am I;
my hands are ready now
to make the earth the place
in which the kingdom comes.
Sent by the Lord am I;
my hands are ready now
to make the earth the place
in which the kingdom comes.

The angels cannot change
a world of hurt and pain
into a world of love,
of justice and of peace.
The task is mine to do,
to set it really free.
Oh, help me to obey;
help me to do your will.

68 SING OF HIS VICTORY

EGYPT

Words: from Revelation 4 & 5
Word & Music
Music: unknown
arranged Geoff Weaver

Gently ♩. = 69

Capo 1(Bm)

1 Sing of his vic-to-ry, tell of his sac-ri-fice:
2 Je-sus, you died for us, pur-chased our li-ber-ty,

wor - thy the Lamb of God who shall re-ceive our love!
made us a priest-ly king-dom, fit to serve our God:

Let ev - ery crea-ture bring true praise to wor-ship him –
from all hu-ma-ni - ty, now to your glo - ry be

hon - our and wis - dom and power for ev - er-more.
hon - our and wis - dom and power for ev - er-more!

> The ancient Egyptian Coptic Church is rich in history and tradition. Its liturgy is
> elaborate and colourful, but there is also a place for simple songs from the heart,
> such as this item of praise. This is most effective as a solo.

Chorus

69 SIYAHAMBA
We are marching

Words: African origin
collected and edited by Anders Nyberg
Music: African melody scored by
Notman KB, Ljungsbro and Lars Parkman

An exuberant song of hope from South Africa which has become popular in recent years.
Experiment with variations in the harmony. It is hard to stand still while singing this song!

Joyfully ♩ = 120

We are march - ing in the light of God,— we are march-ing in the light of God,— we are march-ing in the light of, (the

we are march - ing light of God.)— We are march-ing, (march-ing, we are march-ing, march-ing,) we are march-ing in the light of God!—

OPTIONAL FURTHER VERSES

2 We are living in the love of God . . .

3 We are moving in the power of God . . .

70 TATANACA, MAMANACA, SARANTAÑANI

Men and women, let us walk

BOLIVIA

Words and music: Zoilo Yanapa
arranged Christopher Norton

1 Ta - ta - na - ca, ma - ma - na - ca, Sa - ran - ta - ña - ni!
(2) Igle - sia na - ca - sa - ja ma - ya-ghasi-ña - ni,
1 Men and wo - men, let us walk and let's walk to - ge-ther;
(2) Church be one strong bo - dy, walk-ing to - ge-ther;

Ta - ta - na - ca, ma - ma - na - ca, Sa - ran - ta - ña - ni! Way - na -
ta - ke Igle - sia na - ca - sa - ja ma - ya-ghasi-ña - ni. Ma - ya -
men and wo - men, let us walk and let's walk to - ge-ther. Bro-thers,
let the Church be one strong bo - dy, walk-ing to - ge-ther; ev - ery

- na - ka, ta - wa - co - na - ka, sayt' a - si - ña - ni. Way - na -
- qui,___ ta - ke - ni,___ Sa - ran - ta - ña - ni. Ma - ya -
sis - ters, child-ren and youth, let's all move to - ge - ther; bro-thers,
mem - ber touched by each o - ther, keep-ing to - ge - ther. ev - ery

> This dance-song comes from the Aymara people of Bolivia. With such vitality in their worship, it is not surprising that they are part of the fastest growing church in their country.

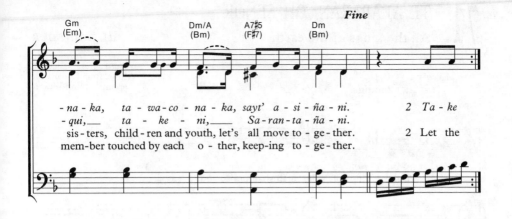

Fine

- na - ka,   ta - wa-co - na - ka,   sayt' a - si - ña - ni.   2 Ta - ke
- qui,___   ta - ke - ni,___   Sa - ran - ta - ña - ni.
sis - ters,   child - ren and youth,   let's all move to - ge - ther.   2 Let the
mem - ber touched by each   o - ther,   keep - ing to - ge - ther.

1 *Tatanaca, mamanaca, Sarantañani!*
   Tatanaca, mamanaca, Sarantañani!
   Waynanaka, tawaconaka, sayt' asiñani.
   Waynanaka, tawaconaka, sayt' asiñani.

2 *Take Iglesia nacasaja mayaghasiñani,*
   take Iglesia nacasaja mayaghasiñani.
   Mayaqui, takeni, Sarantañani.
   Mayaqui, takeni, Sarantañani.

1 Men and women, let us walk
   and let's walk together;
   men and women, let us walk
   and let's walk together.
   Brothers, sisters, children and youth,
   let's all move together;
   brothers, sisters, children and youth,
   let's all move together.

2 Let the Church be one strong body,
   walking together;
   let the Church be one strong body,
   walking together.
   Every member touched by each other,
   keeping together;
   every member touched by each other,
   keeping together.

71 TE ALABARÁN, OH SEÑOR
All the kings of the earth

Words: from Psalm 138
Music: from El Salvador
arranged Geoff Weaver

EL SALVADOR

The people of El Salvador have a long history of suffering and oppression at the hands of the powerful and the wealthy. This joyful psalm of praise is a song of hope and trust in the Lord who 'regards the lowly'. Ideally it should be sung with guitar and light rhythmic accompaniment.

TERI ARADHANA KARU
Lord, in your mercy, remember me

INDIA

Words: after the Indian song
from Psalm 25, Word & Music
Music: unknown
arranged Geoff Weaver

Expressively ♩ = 108

Te - ri a - ra - dha - na_____ ka - ru
Lord, in your mer - cy, re - mem - ber me,

Te - ri a - ra - dha - na_____ ka - ru
Lord, in your mer - cy, re - mem - ber me,

Pa - pa - ksha - ma ker jee - van_____ de - dey
show me your ways, Lord, guide me in your truth and teach me, Lord:

> This is only the refrain of a much longer song originally in Hindi, and sung as a morning prayer. Its character is perhaps best expressed by a solo female voice, as the arranger first heard it hauntingly sung by a young Indian woman.

Teri aradhana karu
Teri aradhana karu
Papakshama ker jeevan dedey
dayaki yachana karu.

Lord, in your mercy, remember me,
Lord, in your mercy, remember me,
show me your ways, Lord,
guide me in your truth and teach me, Lord:
you are my God, my king, my saviour.

Teri aradhana karu.
Teri aradhana karu.

Lord, in your mercy, remember me.
Lord, in your mercy, remember me.

73 THE RIGHT HAND OF GOD

CARIBBEAN

Words: after Patrick Prescord
Word & Music
Music: Noel Dexter
arranged Christopher Norton

Joyfully ♩ = 70

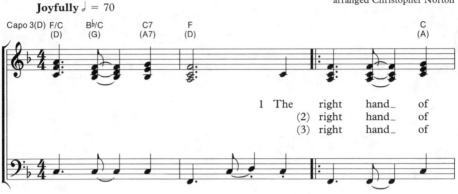

1 The right hand_ of
(2) right hand_ of
(3) right hand_ of

God   is   writ-ing in___ our land,
God   is   point-ing in___ our land,
God   is   strik-ing in___ our land,

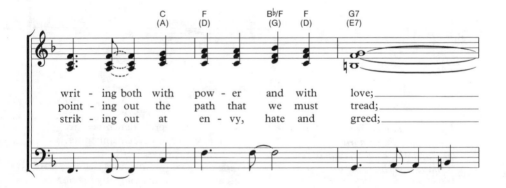

writ - ing both with   pow - er   and with   love;_____
point - ing out the   path that   we must   tread;_____
strik - ing out at   en - vy,   hate and   greed;_____

> A song of judgment, justice and mercy from the Caribbean.
> It is very important to feel the rhythmic freedom here.

our con-flicts and__ our fears, our
so cloud-ed is__ the way, so
our self-ish-ness__ and lust, our

tri-umphs and__ our tears, are re-cord-ed by__ the
ea-si-ly__ we stray, but we're guid-ed by__ the
pride, and deeds un-just are con-demned by__ the

right hand of God.   2 The
right hand of God.   3 The
right hand of God.   4 The

4   The right hand of God is healing in our land,
     healing broken bodies, minds and souls;
       so when we bow in prayer,
       the love of Christ is there
    and we're healed by the right hand of God.

5   The right hand of God is planting in our land,
     planting seeds of freedom, hope and love.
       In this and every place
       all we who live by grace
    can be one with the right hand of God.

74 THUMA MINA
Send me, Lord

SOUTH AFRICA

Words: African origin,
collected and edited by Anders Nyberg
Music: African melody scored by Notman KB,
Ljungsbro and Lars Parkman

Worshipfully ♩ = 100

LEADER
Thu - ma mi - na,
Send me,__ Lord,

ALL
Thu - ma   mi - na   thu - ma   mi   -   na   thu - ma
Send me,   Je - sus   send me,   Je   -   sus   send me,

to repeat

thu - ma mi - na
send   me,__ Lord

to end

mi - na,   So - man - dla.
Je - sus   send me,   Lord

thu - ma   - dla.
Send me,   Lord

LEADER   *Thuma mina,*
ALL   *thuma mina*
         thuma mina
         thuma mina,
         Somandla.

1 LEADER   Send me, Lord:
   ALL   Send me, Jesus
            send me, Jesus
            send me, Jesus
            send me, Lord.

2 LEADER   Lead me, Lord:
   ALL   Lead me, Jesus ...

3 LEADER   Fill me, Lord:
   ALL   Fill me, Jesus ...

Both this and the following setting of the text come from the rich South
African tradition of sacred song which is noted for its harmonies and for its
strength and dignity. Sing these songs unaccompanied and use them in a
variety of ways, e.g. after intercessions, after a talk, at the end of the service.

75 THUMA MINA
Send me, Jesus

SOUTH AFRICA

Words and music:
transcribed from the singing of Lulu Dumazweni
arranged John Bell

As quickly as the mood requires

1 Thu - ma mi - na,___ thu - ma mi - na,___
2 Ndi - ya vu - ma,___ ndi - ya vu - ma,___
1 Send me, Je - sus;___ send me, Je - sus;___
2 I am will - ing,___ I am will - ing;___

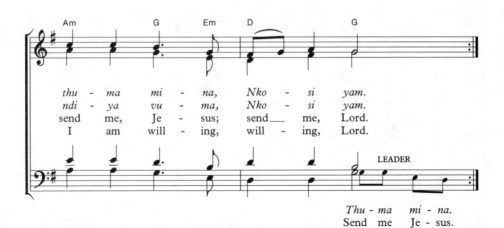

thu - ma mi - na, Nko - si yam.
ndi - ya vu - ma, Nko - si yam.
send me, Je - sus; send___ me, Lord.
I am will - ing, will - ing, Lord.

LEADER

Thu - ma mi - na.
Send me Je - sus.

1 *Thuma mina, thuma mina,*
   thuma mina, Nkosi yam.

2 *Ndiya vuma, ndiya vuma,*
   ndiya vuma, Nkosi yam.

1 Send me, Jesus; send me, Jesus;
   send me, Jesus; send me, Lord.

2 I am willing, I am willing;
   I am willing, willing, Lord.

76 THE LORD IS MY LIGHT

CZECHOSLOVAKIA

Words: from Psalm 27
paraphrased John Bell
Music: Czech hymn tune
arranged Geoff Weaver

Confidently ♩ = 138

1 The Lord___ is my light, my light and
2 Should e - vil powers ad - vance, should arm - ies
3 One thing I ask the Lord. This on - ly
4 Pre - served by God from harm, se - cure in

my sal - va - tion. With God pro - tect - ing me
try to kill,___ let them sur - round me and
I de - sire:___ al - ways in wor - ship to
him a - lone,___ I will re - joice in the

from ev - ery dan - ger, whom shall I___ fear?
let them at - tack me, I'll still trust___ God.
gaze at God's good - ness and seek his___ aid.
face of af - flic - tion and sing God's___ song.

A setting of Psalm 27 based on a 17th century Czech hymn tune and sung, amongst others, by the
Evangelical Church of the Czech Brethren. The minor mode gives it a strength and seriousness of
purpose. It can be sung either in parts or in unison with keyboard accompaniment.

77 TUYOES EL REINO
Yours is the kingdom

ARGENTINA

Words: from the Lord's Prayer
Music: Pablo Sosa
arranged Geoff Weaver

Tu-yo es el rei - no, tu-yo el po - der, tuy - a la glo - riay
Yours is the king - dom, yours is the power, yours is the glo - ry

siem-pre-hide ser, siem-pre-hide ser, siem-pre-hide ser;
for ev - er-more, for ev - er-more, for ev - er-more;

tu-yo es el rei - no, el po - der y la glo-riay siem-pre-hide ser. A - men.
yours is the king-dom, the power and the glo - ry for ev - er-more. A - men.

> The composer Pablo Sosa has written much music for worship with an
> authentically Latin American flavour. Here is the certainty of God's King-
> dom allied to the vitality of the dance. It should be sung with vigour, a
> growing sense of excitement and a guitar and percussion accompaniment.

78 VEM, JESUS NOSA ESPERANÇA
Come to be our hope, Lord Jesus

BRAZIL

Words: Jaci Maraschin
Music: Marcilide de Oliveira Filko
arranged Christopher Norton

Rhythmically

1 Vem, Je - sus nos-sa es - pe - ran - ça nos - sas vi - das li - ber -
2 Vem te - cer um mun - do no - vo nos cam - in - hos de verd - a -
1 Come to be our hope, Lord Je-sus, come to set___ our peo-ple
2 Come to build your new cre - a-tion through the road___ of ser-vant-

- tar.   Vem, nas-cer em nós, cri - an - ça   vem o
- de;   pa - ra que a-fi - nal, o po - vo   vi-va em
free;   from op-pres-sion come, re - lease us,   turn de -
- hood; give new life to ev - ery na - tion,   chang-ing

teu___ po-der nos dar.   Vem, li - ber - ta os pri - sio -
ple - na li-berd - ade.   Vem, Je - sus, a - bre o fu -
- feat___ to vic-to - ry!   Come, re - lease from ev - ery
e - vil in-to good.   Come and o - pen our to -

Jaci Maraschin is one of Brazil's foremost Church composers. For him the dance finds its place in worship reflecting hope, while the flattened third portrays the pain of oppression. A light rhythmic accompaniment helps to bring out the dance-like character here.

Words and music: © 1989 World Council of Churches, Geneva

Words: Spanish Jorge Rodríguez
English translation Jaci Maraschin

Eb (D) Fm/Ab (Em) G7 (F#7) Cm (Bm) Eb7 (D7)

- nei - ros   da in-jus - ti - ça e da a - fli - ção;   vem, re -
- tu - ro   do teu reino de a - leg - ri - a.   Vem, der -
pri - son   those who suf - fer in our land: In your
- mor - row   for a king - dom now so near;   take a -

Ab (G) Bb (A) Eb (D) Cb (Bb) Ab (G) Bb (A) Eb (D)

- ú - ne os bra - si - lei - ros   em a - mor___ e em com-preen-são.
- ruba o i-men - so mu - ro   que se - para___ a noite e o dia.
love we find the rea-son still to live___ and un - der-stand.
- way all hu - man sor-row – give us hope___ in place of fear.

1 Vem, Jesus nossa esperança
   nossas vidas libertar.
   Vem, nascer em nós, criança
   vem o teu poder nos dar.
   Vem, liberta os prisioneiros
   da injustiça e da aflição;
   vem, reúne os brasi leiros
   em amor e em compreensão.

2 Vem tecer um mundo novo
   nos caminhos de verdade;
   para que, afinal, o povo
   viva em plena liberdade.
   Vem, Jesus, abre o futuro
   do teu reino de alegria.
   Vem, derruba o imenso muro
   que separa a noite e o dia.

1 Come to be our hope, Lord Jesus,
   come to set our people free;
   from oppression come, release us,
   turn defeat to victory!
   Come, release from every prison
   those who suffer in our land:
   In your love we find the reason
   still to live and understand.

2 Come to build your new creation
   through the road of servanthood;
   give new life to every nation,
   changing evil into good.
   Come and open our tomorrow
   for a kingdom now so near;
   take away all human sorrow –
   give us hope in place of fear.

79 WA WA WA EMIMIMO
Come, O Holy Spirit, come

NIGERIA

Words and music: unknown
arranged Geoff Weaver

Wa wa wa E-mi-mi-mo.
Come, O Ho-ly Spi-rit, come.

E-mi-o-lo-ye
Ho-ly Spi-rit, come.

Wa wa wa A-lag-ba-
Come, Al-might-y Spi-rit,

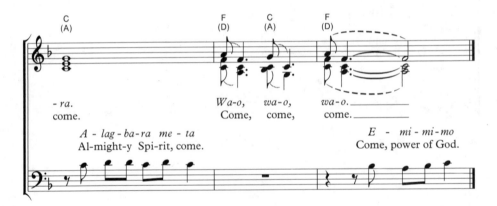

-ra.
come.

A - lag-ba-ra me - ta
Al-might-y Spi-rit, come.

Wa-o, wa-o, wa-o.
Come, come, come.

E - mi - mi-mo
Come, power of God.

Wa wa wa Emimimo.
Wa wa wa Alagbara.
Wao, wao, wao.

Come, O Holy Spirit, come.
Come, Almighty Spirit, come.
Come, come, come.

First 3 times: sing at slow tempo ♩ = 88: 1. top line only (with tenor response); 2. add lower alto; 3. add guitar (first beat of every bar only). 4th time onwards sing faster at ♩ = 120. Add the middle part then percussion and more rhythmic guitar.

This Yoruba invocation of the Holy Spirit is very effective when sung slowly and quietly, gradually introducing voices and instruments on each repetition as indicated. A change of tempo with drums and clapping provides an exciting conclusion, always greeted with enthusiasm by Africans.

80 WHAT A MIGHTY GOD WE SERVE

SOUTH AFRICA

Words: unknown
Music: Zulu working song
arranged Peter Sandwell

With a strength and joy ♩ = 140

1 What a might - y God we serve,___ what a
2 He cre - a - ted you and me,___ he cre -
3 He has all the power to save,___ he has
4 Let us praise the liv - ing God,___ let us
5 What a might - y God we serve,___ what a

might - y God we serve,___ what a might - y God we serve,
- a - ted you and me,___ he cre - a - ted you and me,___
all the power to save,___ he has all the power to save,___
praise the liv - ing God,___ let us praise the liv - ing God,_
might - y God we serve,___ what a might - y God we serve,

___ what___ a might - y God we serve.___
___ he___ cre - a - ted you and me.___
___ he___ has all the power to save.___
___ let___ us praise the liv - ing God.___
___ what___ a might - y God we serve.___

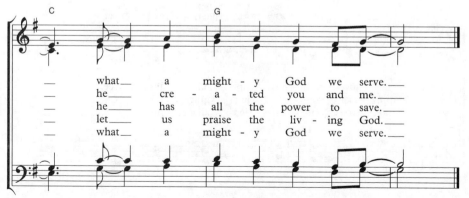

> A strong Zulu song of affirmation from South Africa.

Music arrangement: © 1986 Peter Sandwell,
PS! Productions Dalskog 570 22 Forsenum, Sweden

81 WHEN I BEHOLD JESUS
What kind of love

SOUTH AMERICA

Words: adapted Word & Music
Music: Almaz Belhu
arranged Geoff Weaver

Flowing ♩. = 66

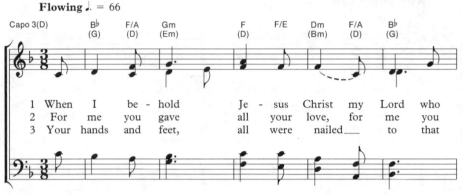

1 When I be-hold Je - sus Christ my Lord who
2 For me you gave all your love, for me you
3 Your hands and feet, all were nailed___ to that

died for me,_____ I am a - mazed
suf - fered pain;_____ I find no words –
rug - ged cross;_____ you died my death,

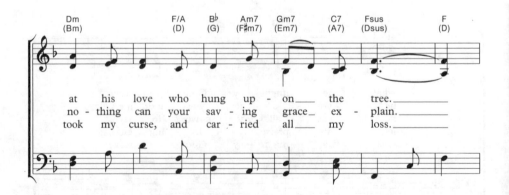

at his love who hung up - on___ the tree._____
no - thing can your sav - ing grace_ ex - plain._____
took my curse, and car - ried all___ my loss._____

> This pentatonic melody from South America
> requires an easy expressive flow.

1st time SOLO
2nd time HARMONY

What kind of love_ is this;_____ what kind of love_ is

this?_____ You showed your love,_ Je - sus, love for me on

Cal - va - ry._____ What me on Cal - va - ry._____

4   You had no sin, holy Lamb,
    but you were tortured, tried;
    on Golgotha once for all,
    O Son of God, you died.
        What kind of love . . .

5   Incarnate Lord, love come down
    to walk our earthly ways:
    we worship you, speak your name,
    and lift to heaven our praise.
        What kind of love . . .

82 WINTER HAS GONE

CHINA

Words: from Song of Solomon 2,
after Wang Wei-fan
Music: Jia-ou Shengben Lina
arranged Geoff Weaver

1 Win-ter has gone, the night is through, flo-wers are bloom-ing, all birds sing. Why should I wait with doubt and fear? A-rise, my Lord, I'll go with you!

2 Re-veal your light that I may see, your still small voice that I may hear; and like a dove, let joy and peace and love des-cend to dwell with me.

3 And so, my Lord, my mas-ter true, a-mong the flowers of pa-ra-dise I'll find you in the sec-ret place, and in your mer-cy go with you.

The verses of this hymn were written before the cultural revolution in China.
The refrain written in 1982 sings of the dark veil of those years which brought
suffering and death to so many in China, but a dramatic growth in the Church.

'Winter has passed' from Sound the Bamboo

Music: © 1982 Asian Institute for Liturgy and Music   Words: after Wang Wei-fan © Word & Music / Jubilate Hymns

1 Winter has gone, the night is through,
   flowers are blooming, all birds sing.
   Why should I wait with doubt and fear?
   Arise, my Lord, I'll go with you!
     Jesus my joy, my hope, my all,
     my love, my life eternally:
     through death's dark night, close by my side,
     O dearest Lord, be close to me.

2 Reveal your light that I may see,
   your still small voice that I may hear;
   and like a dove, let joy and peace
   and love descend to dwell with me.
     Jesus my Lord . . .

3 And so, my Lord, my master true,
   among the flowers of paradise
   I'll find you in the secret place,
   and in your mercy go with you.
     Jesus my Lord . . .

83 YESU YU HAI LEO
Jesus is alive today

EAST AFRICA

Words and music: unknown
arranged David Peacock

Lively ♩ = 115

Ye - su yu ha - i le - o Ye - su yu ha - i le - o Ye - su
Je - sus is a - live to - day, Je - sus is a - live to - day, Je - sus

yu ha - i le - o a - si - fi - we._____ Ye - su
is a - live to - day – O praise his name!_____ Je - sus

yu ha - i le - o Ye - su yu ha - i le - o Ye - su
is a - live to - day, Je - sus is a - live to - day, Je - sus

yu ha - i le - o a - si - fi - we.
is a - live to - day – O praise his name!

An exuberant song from East Africa suitable for Easter Day, or indeed for any day. Harmonies, descants and drum rhythms will naturally suggest themselves.

Al-le - lu-ya,____ al-le - lu-ya, al-le - lu-ya a - si - fi -
Al-le - lu-ia,____ al-le - lu-ia, al-le - lu-ia – O praise his

- we.____ Al - le - lu - ya,____
name!____ Al - le - lu - ia,____

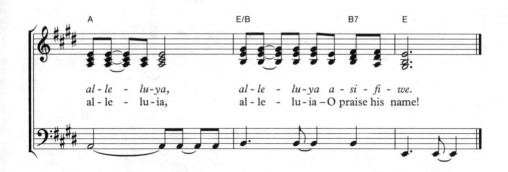

al - le - lu-ya, al - le - lu-ya a - si - fi - we.
al - le - lu-ia, al - le - lu-ia – O praise his name!

Yesu yu hai leo	Jesus is alive today,
Yesu yu hai leo	Jesus is alive today,
Yesu yu hai leo	Jesus is alive today –
asifiwe.	O praise his name!
Yesu yu hai leo . . .	Jesus is alive . . .
Alleluya, alleluya, alleluya	Alleluia, alleluia, alleluia –
asifiwe.	O praise his name!
Alleluya . . .	Alleluia . . .

84 YOUR KINGDOM COME, O LORD

C.I.S.

Words and music: N. Zabolotski
arranged John Bell

Steadily

Your king-dom come, O Lord. Your king-dom come, O Lord. Your

king-dom come, O Lord.__ Your king-dom come, O Lord.

Your kingdom come, O Lord.
Your kingdom come, O Lord.
Your kingdom come, O Lord.
Your kingdom come, O Lord.

Written for a W.C.C. Conference in Melbourne in 1980, the composer Nicolai Zabolotski asked that the song should start softly, almost in a questioning way, and should grow in strength and confidence until the final phrase which asserts the hope that God's Kingdom is coming.

Copyright Addresses

Asian Institute for Liturgy and Music, PO Box 10533, Quezon City 1112, Philippines

Associaton Ediciones La Aurora, 1244 Buenos Aires, Argentina

Baptist Association of El Salvador, Avenida Sierre Nevade no 922, Colonia Miramonte (Apartado Postal 347), San Salvador, El Salvador

A & C Black (Publishers) Ltd, Howard Road, Eaton Socon, Huntingdon, Cambs PE19 3EZ, UK

Caribbean Conference of Churches, PO Box 616, Bridgetown, Barbados, West Indies

Gerhard Cartford, 2279 Commonwealth Avenue, St Paul, MN 55108, USA

Christ Church Gospel Band, Diocese of Enugu, Christ Church Parish, Uwani, PMB 424, Enugu, Nigera

Christian Conference of Asia, Central Office, G/F 2 Jordan Road, Kowloon, Hong Kong

Dave Dargie, Melunsinenstrasse 13, 8000 Munchen 80, Germany

Faber Music Ltd, 3 Queen Square, London WC1N 2AU, UK

Miss A S Fookes, 82 Streathbourne Road, London SW17 8QY, UK

Hope Publishing Company, 380 South Main Place, Carol Stream, IL 60188, USA

Iona Community, Community House, Pearce Institute, Govan, Glasgow G51 3UU, UK

Jubilate Hymns, Mrs B Grundy, 61 Chessel Avenue, Southampton SO2 4DY, UK. In the USA Jubilate Hymns copyrights are administered by Hope Publishing Company. (See above)

Geonyeng Lee, The Korean National Institute of Arts, 700 Seocho-Dong, Seocho-ku, Seoul, Korea

Leosong Copyright Music Service, Suite 8, Westmead House, Westmead Road, Sutton, Surrey SM1 4JH, UK

Lutheran World Federation, PO Box 2100, 150 Route de Ferney, CH-1211, Geneva 20, Switzerland

Patrick Matsikenyiri, Mutambara Mission, Postbag 2003G, Cashel, Zimbabwe

G Mxadana, c/o ISM (Pty) Ltd, PO Box 1419, Johannesburg 2000, Republic of South Africa

Miss Dinah Reindorf, PO Box 13060, Accra, Ghana

Szokolay Sandor, H 1112 Hegyal ja U770, Budapest, Hungary

Peter Sandwell, 'PS' Production, Dalskog, 570 22 Forserum, Sweden

Melchizik and Mutya Solis, 104 E Lamar Street, Salinary, CA 93906, USA

Pablos Sosa, Camacua 282, 1406 Buenos Aires, Argentina

Stainer & Bell Ltd, PO Box 110, Victoria House, 23 Gruneisen Road, London N3 1DZ, UK

Erzsebet Turmezei, Karácsony Sándor utca 31-22, H-1086, Budapest, Hungary

World Council of Churches, Communications Department, 150 Route de Ferney, CH-1211 Geneva 20, Switzerland

Zeilo Yanapa, Cepita, Casilla 10221, La Paz, Bolivia

Nan Young-Soo, c/o National Council of Churches in Korea, PO Box 134, Seoul, Korea

Orof Nikolai Zabolotski, 27B Chemin Terrinx, 1218 Geneva, Switzerland

Area and Country Index

Index of First Lines

Italics indicate alternative titles